# Amos™ 5.0 Update to the Amos User's Guide

## James L. Arbuckle

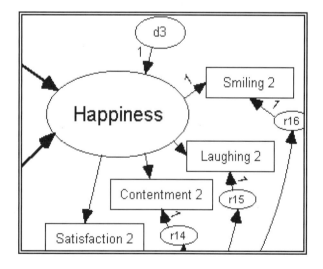

For more information, please contact:

| | |
|---|---|
| Marketing Department | SmallWaters Corporation |
| SPSS Inc. | 1507 E. 53$^{rd}$ Street, #452 |
| 233 S. Wacker Dr., 11$^{th}$ Floor | Chicago, IL 60615, U.S.A. |
| Chicago, IL 60606-6307, U.S.A. | Tel: (773) 667-8635 |
| Tel: (312) 651-3000 | Fax: (773) 955-6252 |
| Fax: (312) 651-3668 | URL: http://www.smallwaters.com |
| URL: http://www.spss.com | |

ISBN 1-56827-322-3

# Contents

# New Features

## Specification search

Structural equation modeling (SEM) is an intrinsically confirmatory technique, but in practice it is often used in an exploratory way. Various tools have been developed for adapting this confirmatory technique to exploratory uses (MacCallum, 1986). These include the use of modification indices and Lagrange multiplier tests for selectively adding parameters to a model, and the use of $z$ statistics (also called critical ratios) and Wald tests for selectively eliminating parameters (Bentler, 1989; Jöreskog & Sörbom, 1996).

Amos 5 provides an additional approach to exploratory SEM. In this approach, exploratory SEM is treated as a problem in model selection in which the number of candidate models is permitted to be large. Tools are provided for systematically fitting many candidate models and for choosing among them on the basis of fit, parsimony, and interpretability.

### Tools for model evaluation

When conducting a specification search, the primary concern is model comparison rather than the evaluation of a single model by itself. For the purpose of model comparison, Amos provides

- extensive tabular and graphic summaries of comparative model fit and its relationship to number of parameters

- rescaled versions of **AIC**, **BCC**, and **BIC**

- Akaike weights based on either **AIC** or **BCC**

- Bayes factors

- a scree test similar to the scree test used in factor analysis (Cattell, 1966)

Amos 5 also provides additional statistics for evaluating models in absolute terms (as distinguished from model comparison). Amos 5 fits alternative "null" or "baseline" models in addition to the usual zero-correlation baseline model. Each alternative baseline model gives rise to an alternative value for such fit measures as **CFI** that depend upon comparison to a baseline model.

## Specification of candidate models

Candidate models can be specified in two different ways. First, just as in earlier versions of Amos, each individual candidate model can be specified as a set of equality constraints on model parameters. In Amos Graphics, you can do this by choosing **Model-Fit→Manage Models** from the menu bar. In Amos Basic, you can do this using the **Model** method. It is possible to specify hundreds or thousands of candidate models in this way, but to do so would be time consuming and would inevitably lead to mistakes.

Amos 5 introduces a second method for specifying candidate models. In this alternative approach, some single- and double-headed arrows in a path diagram are designated as optional. When optional arrows are present, Amos fits the model both with and without each optional arrow, using every possible subset of them. If only one arrow is optional then an exploratory analysis consists of fitting the model with and without the optional arrow. If there are, say, three optional arrows, the program fits the model eight (that is, $2^3$) times, using every possible subset of the optional arrows.

An analysis can be more or less exploratory, depending on how many arrows are optional. Of course, there is a practical limit to the number of optional arrows since each optional arrow doubles the number of models that need to be fitted.

# Assisted multiple-group analysis

When you have data from multiple groups, you often start by asking if it is necessary to draw a separate path diagram for each group, or if the same path diagram will do for all groups. If you conclude that all the groups share the same path diagram, you can proceed to ask whether parameter values are invariant across groups. For example, if you are studying boys and girls, you might want to know whether boys and girls have the same regression weights, or if only certain regression weights are the same for boys and girls. Of course there are also variances and covariances as well as regression weights to consider. Because of the large number of possible cross-group constraints, it is necessary to have a strategy for deciding which cross-group constraints are worth testing and in what order to test them. Bollen (1989), Kline (1998), and others discuss such strategies. Amos 5 implements an automatic procedure for generating a nested hierarchy of models in which cross-group constraints are introduced incrementally in a pre-chosen order.

No automatic procedure can anticipate the purpose of an individual study. If necessary, you can modify Amos's automatically generated cross-group constraints to suit the needs of an individual study. However, no such customization will be necessary in most cases. You also have the option of performing multiple-group analyses by imposing cross-group constraints manually, just as in Amos 4.

# Enhanced text output

The content of the Amos 5 output file is the same as in Amos 4, but the new output viewer includes additional navigational aids, display options, and table formatting options.

## Navigation panel

In Figure 1, the output viewer displays a portion of the output from an analysis with two groups and two models. In this example, the navigation panel on the left has been used to select bootstrap standard errors associated with variance estimates for 'Group number 1' and 'Model A'.

*Figure 1: Amos 5 output viewer*

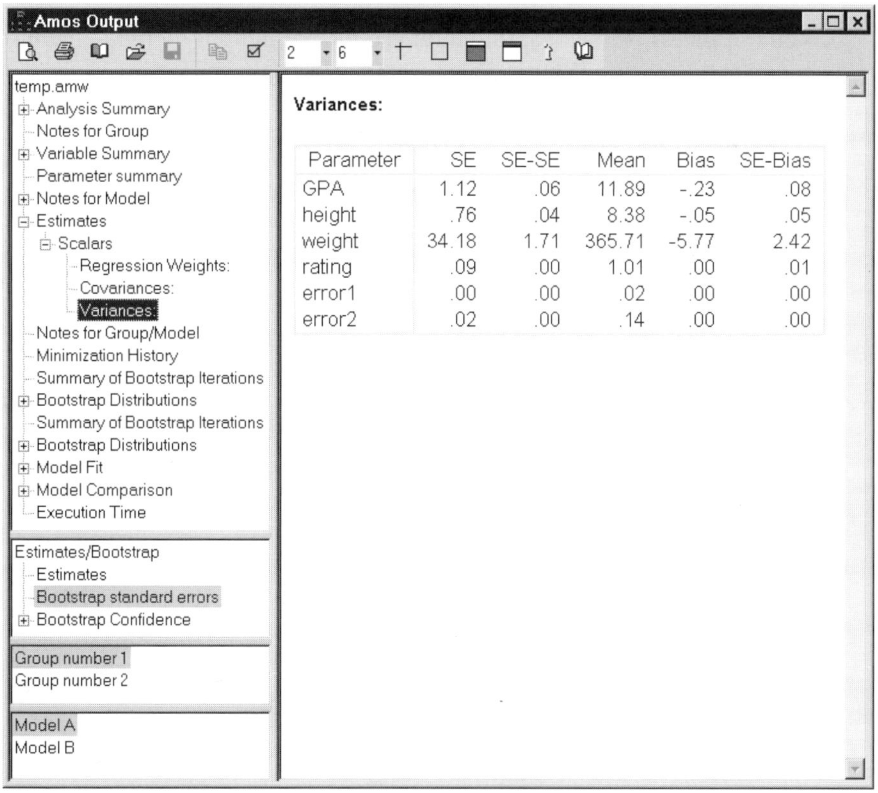

Amos Output

temp.amw
Analysis Summary
Notes for Group
Variable Summary
Parameter summary
Notes for Model
Estimates
  Scalars
    Regression Weights:
    Covariances:
    Variances:
Notes for Group/Model
Minimization History
Summary of Bootstrap Iterations
Bootstrap Distributions
Summary of Bootstrap Iterations
Bootstrap Distributions
Model Fit
Model Comparison
Execution Time

Estimates/Bootstrap
Estimates
Bootstrap standard errors
Bootstrap Confidence

Group number 1
Group number 2

Model A
Model B

**Variances:**

| Parameter | SE | SE-SE | Mean | Bias | SE-Bias |
|-----------|------|-------|--------|-------|---------|
| GPA | 1.12 | .06 | 11.89 | -.23 | .08 |
| height | .76 | .04 | 8.38 | -.05 | .05 |
| weight | 34.18 | 1.71 | 365.71 | -5.77 | 2.42 |
| rating | .09 | .00 | 1.01 | .00 | .01 |
| error1 | .00 | .00 | .02 | .00 | .00 |
| error2 | .02 | .00 | .14 | .00 | .00 |

## Toolbar

The new toolbar in the output viewer includes tools you can use to

- display a print preview of the output file

- print the output file

- change the page format for printing (paper size, margins, and so on)

- open a different output file

- copy the current selection to the Clipboard

- choose whether to view the entire output file, or just the portion that is selected in the navigation panel (as seen in Figure 1)

- choose whether to show variable names or labels (when available), and choose formatting options for names and labels

- specify the number of decimal places used for displaying numerical results

- specify the spacing between table columns

- specify table formatting

You can access online help for individual toolbar buttons by right-clicking the button and choosing **What's This?** from the popup menu.

## Context-sensitive help

Many section and table headings have help topics associated with them. When you pass the mouse over an item that has a help topic associated with it, the text displays as a link and the pointer changes to a hand. Click the link to view the help topic.

## Use-it-in-a-sentence help

Some numbers have English-language usage examples associated with them. When you pass the mouse over a number that has an example associated with it, the number displays as a link and the pointer changes to a hand. Click the link to view the example.

## Popup menu

The output viewer includes a popup menu, which you can access by clicking anywhere in the output viewer and then right-clicking. The popup menu includes the following commands:

- **Select**: Selects that portion of the output file. For example, clicking within a table selects the entire table. You can then copy the selection to the Clipboard, or drag it to another location.

- **Copy**: Copies the portion of the output file that you clicked to the Clipboard. For example, clicking within a table copies the entire table to the Clipboard.

- **Show Path**: Displays an XPATH expression for the portion of the output file you clicked. This is useful for users who write programs to extract information from Amos output files. For more information, see **XHTML format**, below.

## XHTML format

The text output file is in XHTML format, which provides the following benefits:

- Table formatting is preserved when you use the Clipboard or drag-and-drop editing to copy tables to other applications.

- XHTML formatted files can serve as an archival format. To view an Amos output file in a browser such as Internet Explorer, Netscape, or Opera, change the file extension from **AmosOutput** to **htm** or **html**.

- Amos output can be parsed by an XML parser. If you are writing a program to post-process Amos output, you can use an XPATH expression to extract any desired portion of the output; for example, the table of standardized indirect effects for the group called "Group number 1" and the model called "Model A".

# Accessibility

Font, color, and other accessibility settings for Internet Explorer affect the Amos 5 output viewer. You can change these settings in two ways:

1. From within Internet Explorer, choose **Tools**→**Internet Options** from the menu bar.

2. From within Amos Graphics, click ☑ on the output viewer toolbar. On the **View** tab of the **Options** dialog box, click **Internet Options**.

If you wish to provide additional visual cues when color is used as a distinctive graphical feature, choose **View/Set**→**Interface Properties** from the Amos Graphics menu bar, click the **Accessibility** tab, and then select the **Alternative to color** checkbox. This will

- display optional arrows as dashed in specification searches

- use thick lines to draw color-highlighted objects in assisted multiple-group analyses

# Improved Amos Basic editor

The improved Amos Basic editor includes new features that make it easier to write and debug Amos Basic programs.

## Statement completion

Statement completion saves keystrokes. When you start typing a statement, Amos 5 presents a list of objects, methods, and variables you can use to complete the statement. To use an item from the list, double-click it.

For example, if you start a line by typing "dim x as ", Amos Basic displays a list that includes **AmosDebug**, **AmosEngine**, and **PathDiagrammer**.

Suppose your program already contains the line "Dim Sem as New AmosEngine". If you type "sem.", Amos Basic displays a list of **AmosEngine** methods you can use to complete the statement.

## Syntax ToolTips

Syntax ToolTips give you on-the-fly information about the command you are entering.

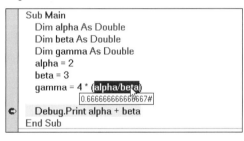

```
Option Explicit
Dim Sem As AmosEngine

Sub Main
    Set Sem = New AmosEngine

    Sem.BeginGroup |
End Su BeginGroup( FileName As String, [TableName As String], [GroupingVariable],
              [GroupingValue] )
```

## Hover evaluation

Hover evaluation lets you move the mouse over a variable and see its value in a ToolTip. In the following figure, the program has stopped at a breakpoint. Holding the mouse pointer over the expression "alpha/beta" displays the value of that expression.

```
Sub Main
    Dim alpha As Double
    Dim beta As Double
    Dim gamma As Double
    alpha = 2
    beta = 3
    gamma = 4 * (alpha/beta)
                0.666666666666667#
    Debug.Print alpha + beta
End Sub
```

# New toolbar

The Amos Graphics toolbar provides one-click access to the most frequently used tools.

By default, when you first launch Amos Graphics, the menu bar is docked across the top of the window, but you can dock either the toolbar or menu bar on any edge, or display them as floating palettes. Both are fully customizable.

## Associating a macro with a toolbar button or menu item

You can associate a toolbar button, menu item, or hot key with any Amos macro, including those you write yourself. This example shows you how to create a toolbar button that lets you access the **Name Unobserved Variables** macro with a single click:

➔  Choose **Tools→Customize** from the Amos Graphics menu bar.

➔  In the **Customize** dialog box, click the **Commands** tab.

➡️ In the **Categories** box, click **Macros** to select it.

➡️ In the **Commands** box, locate the macro **Name Unobserved Variables** and drag it to the desired location on the toolbar. A drop line indicates where the macro button will appear when you release the mouse button.

If you drag **Name Unobserved Variables** to the beginning of the second row of buttons, the toolbar will look something like this:

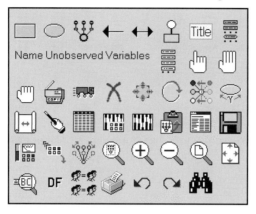

**Tip:** You an also drag a macro onto a menu. When you drag a macro to a menu, the menu drops, allowing you to place the macro command wherever you choose.

## Adding an image to a toolbar button

By default, the new toolbar button displays the name of the macro. If you prefer, you can display an image in addition to the text, or even display an image instead of the text.

The previous example showed you how to create a toolbar button for the macro **Name Unobserved Variables**. This example shows you how to add an image to the new button.

➡️ On the toolbar, right-click **Name Unobserved Variables** and choose **Image and Text** from the popup menu. A checkmark indicates that it is enabled.

**Note:** The **Image and Text** command is only available when the **Customize** dialog box is open. If you have closed the **Customize** dialog box, you can reopen it by right-clicking the toolbar button and choosing **Customize** from the popup menu.

➡️ Copy the bitmap you want to use to the Clipboard. This example uses one of the Amos sample images:

- In Windows Explorer, browse to the location where you installed Amos (for example, **C:\Program Files\Amos 5**). Locate the file **LozengeFilled.bmp** in the Sample Graphics folder, and open it in Microsoft Paint.

- In Microsoft Paint, choose **Edit→Select All** from the menu bar, and then choose **Edit→Copy**.

- Close Microsoft Paint.

➔ In **Amos Graphics**, right-click the **Name Unobserved Variables** button on the toolbar, and choose **Paste Button Image** from the popup menu.

The macro button now displays both the text, **Name Unobserved Variables**, and the graphic ◆.

➔ In the **Customize** dialog box, click **Close**.

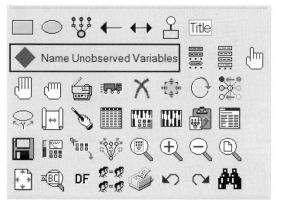

## Associating a macro with a shortcut key

You can also use the keyboard to execute macros. This example shows you how to associate the **Name Unobserved Variables** macro with the key combination Alt+Ctrl+K.

➔ Choose **Tools→Customize** from the Amos Graphics menu bar.

➔ In the **Customize** dialog box, click **Keyboard**.

➔ In the **Customize Keyboard** dialog box, click **Macros** in the **Categories** box.

➔ Click **Name Unobserved Variables** in the **Commands** box.

➔ Enter the new key combination in the **Press New Shortcut Key** box. For example, to enter Alt+Ctrl+K, press and hold down the Alt button, the Ctrl button, and the K button in that order. When all three are depressed, release them. If you make an error while entering the combination, use the **Backspace** key to clear your entry.

The **Press New Shortcut Key** box displays the new key combination.

➔ Click **Assign**.

➔ Click **Close**.

# Random number generation

For some purposes, Amos 5 uses the random number generator known as the Mersenne Twister (Matsumoto & Nishimura, 1998). Specifically, the Mersenne Twister is used

- during heuristic specification searches to break ties between equally well-fitting models

- as the uniform random number generator for the **AmosRanGen** class (see **Enhanced programmability**, below)

You can specify a seed for the Mersenne Twister by choosing **Tools→Seed Manager** from the Amos Graphics menu bar.

For all other purposes, the Wichman-Hill (1982) random number generator is used, as in Amos 4.

# Enhanced programmability

Seventy-one new classes and class members provide additional programmatic control over Amos. They are documented in the online help and also in the file **Programming Reference.pdf**, which is located in the **Documentation** folder of the Amos installation. If you performed a typical installation, the path will be **C:\Program Files\Amos 5\Documentation**.

# Improved online help

The online help has been expanded and extensively cross-referenced to provide you with the help you need when you need it.

# Control over variable labels in path diagrams

Amos 5 includes an option that lets you easily show or hide all variable labels in a path diagram.

→ Choose **View/Set→Interface Properties** from the Amos Graphics menu bar.

→ In the **Interface Properties** dialog box, click the **Misc** tab.

→ Select or clear the **Display variable labels** checkbox.

→ Click **Apply**.

# Acknowledgments

Patrick Michael Bernet performed quality assurance testing and reviewed this user's guide update. Tor Neilands provided suggestions and bug reports as he did for previous Amos versions. In particular, Tor improved the new output viewer and the interface for automated multiple-groups analysis through his criticisms of early versions of those features. Numerous users of preliminary versions of the program provided valuable feedback, including Carolyn Ahlstrom, John Antonakis, Stephen J. Aragon, Christopher Bratt, Noelle C. Chiang, Wynne W. Chin, Jan-Eric Gustafsson, Abhijit Jain, Yutaka Kano, Kyle Kercher, Doyoung Kim, Kristie Koenig, Günter Maier, Bryan R. Niederberger, Julie Hicks Patrick, Darleen Pawlowicz, Joe Petrone, Dale Pietrzak, Rachel Pruchno, Chris Sheldrick, Carter Smith, Yan Tian, Robert J. Vandenberg, and Grover J. Whitehurst.

The specification search feature benefited from suggestions by EunYoung Cho, Meredith Coles, Brigette Erwin, Tiffany Floyd, Malati Gadgil, Shruti Gupta, Yahaira Marquez Perez, Jill Teitelbaum, Kimberley Merriman, Denise Ogden, Charles Parrish, Julie Pirsch, Gerald Ross, and Jennifer Silk.

Sara Gruen edited the user's guide update.

# Example 22: Specification Search

## Purpose

- Demonstrate a largely confirmatory specification search (with few optional arrows).
- Demonstrate a largely exploratory specification search (with many optional arrows).

## The data

This example uses the Felson and Bohrnstedt (1979) girls' data, previously used in Example 7.

## The model

The initial model for the specification search comes from Felson and Bohrnstedt (1979), as seen in Figure 2:

*Figure 2: Felson and Bohrnstedt's model for girls*

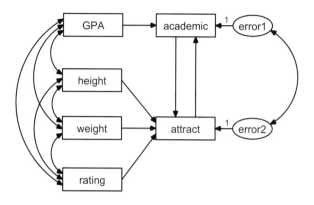

## Specification search with few optional arrows

Felson and Bohrnstedt were primarily interested in the two single-headed arrows, **academic←attract** and **attract←academic**. The question was whether one or both, or possibly neither, of the arrows was needed. For this reason, you will make both arrows optional during this specification search. The double-headed arrow connecting **error1** and **error2** is an undesirable feature of the model because it complicates the interpretation of the effects represented by the single-headed arrows, and so you will also make it optional. The specification search will help to decide which of these three optional arrows, if any, are essential to the model.

This specification search is largely confirmatory in the sense that most arrows are required by the model, and only three are optional.

### ❑ Specify the model

➔ Choose **File→Open** from the Amos Graphics menu bar.

➔ In the **Open** dialog box, double-click the file **Ex22a.amw**. If you performed a typical installation, the path will be **C:\Program Files\Amos 5\Examples\Ex22a.amw**.

The path diagram for the model opens in the Drawing Area. Initially, there are no optional arrows, as seen in Figure 2.

### ❑ Open the Specification Search window

➔ Click 🔍 on the Amos Graphics toolbar, or choose **Model-Fit→Specification Search** from the menu bar.

This opens the **Specification Search** window. Initially, only the toolbar is visible, as seen here:

## ❑ Explore the on-line help

➜ To get acquainted with the help system, right-click a few buttons on the **Specification Search** toolbar, and choose **What's This?** and **Help** from the popup menu.

> What's This?
> Help

## ❑ Make some arrows optional

➜ Click ⬚ on the **Specification Search** toolbar, and then click the double-headed arrow that connects **error1** and **error2**. The arrow changes color to indicate that the arrow is optional.

**Tip:** If you want the optional arrow to appear as dashed as well as colored, as seen below, choose **View/Set→Interface Properties** from the Amos Graphics menu bar, and then on the **Accessibility** tab, select the **Alternative to color** checkbox.

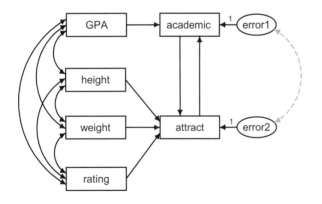

➜ To make the arrow required again, click ▬ on the **Specification Search** toolbar, and then click the arrow. When you move the pointer away, the arrow will again display as a required arrow.

➜ Click the ⬚ tool again, and then click the arrows in your path diagram until it looks like the following:

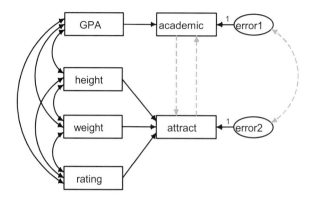

When you perform the exploratory analysis later on, the program will treat the three colored arrows as optional and will try to fit the model using every possible subset of them.

## ❑ Select program options

➔ Click ☑ on the **Specification Search** toolbar.

➔ In the **Options** dialog box, click the **Current results** tab.

➔ Click **Reset** to ensure that your options are the same as those used in this example.

| Options | ✕ |
|---|---|

Current results | Next search | Appearance

Display

☑ Ignore inadmissibility and instability

☑ Model number
☑ Model name
☑ Params
☑ df
☑ C
☑ C - df
☐ AIC

☑ Show saturated model

☐ Show null models

☑ Keep on top

Reset

BCC, AIC, BIC
- ○ Raw
- ● Zero-based (min = 0)
- ○ Akaike weights / Bayes factors (max = 1)
- ○ Akaike weights / Bayes factors (sum = 1)

➔ Now click the **Next search** tab. The text at the top indicates that the exploratory analysis will fit eight (i.e., $2^3$) models.

➔ In the **Retain only the best ___ models** number box, change the value from **10** to **0**.

With a default value of 10, the specification search reports at most ten 1-parameter models, at most ten 2-parameter models, and so on. If the value is set to 0, there is no limitation on the number of models reported.

Limiting the number of models reported can speed up a specification search significantly. However, only eight models in total will be encountered during the specification search for this example, and specifying a non-zero value for **Retain only the best ___ models** would have the undesirable side-effect of inhibiting the program from normalizing Akaike weights and Bayes factors so that they sum to one across all models, as seen later.

**Options**

Current results | Next search | Appearance

8 models will be fitted

- ⦿ All subsets    ○ Stepwise
- ○ Forward       ○ Backward

0  Use no more than ___ optional parameters.

0  Retain only the best ___ models.

Benchmark models

☑ Saturated
☑ Null 1
☑ Null 2
☑ Null 3
☑ Null 4

➔ Close the **Options** dialog box.

## ❑ Perform the specification search

➔ Click ▶ on the **Specification Search** toolbar. The program fits the model eight times, using every subset of the optional arrows. When it finishes, the **Specification Search** window expands to show the results.

The following table summarizes fit measures for the eight models and the saturated model.

| Model | Params | df | C | C-df | BCC$_0$ | BIC$_0$ | C/df | p | Notes |
|---|---|---|---|---|---|---|---|---|---|
| 1 | 19 | 2 | 2.761 | 0.761 | 3.830 | 10.375 | 1.381 | 0.251 | |
| 2 | 18 | 3 | 19.155 | 16.155 | 18.154 | 21.427 | 6.385 | 0.000 | |
| 3 | 17 | 4 | 19.215 | 15.215 | 16.144 | 16.144 | 4.804 | 0.001 | |
| 4 | 16 | 5 | 67.342 | 62.342 | 62.201 | 58.929 | 13.468 | 0.000 | |
| 5 | 17 | 4 | 27.911 | 23.911 | 24.840 | 24.840 | 6.978 | 0.000 | |
| 6 | 18 | 3 | 2.763 | -0.237 | 1.761 | 5.034 | 0.921 | 0.430 | |
| 7 | 17 | 4 | 3.071 | -0.929 | 0.000 | 0.000 | 0.768 | 0.546 | |
| 8 | 18 | 3 | 2.895 | -0.105 | 1.894 | 5.167 | 0.965 | 0.408 | |
| Sat | 21 | 0 | 0.000 | 0.000 | 5.208 | 18.299 | | | |

The **Model** column contains an arbitrary index number from 1 through 8 for each of the models fitted during the specification search. **Sat** identifies the saturated model. Looking at the first row, Model 1 has 19 parameters and 2 degrees of freedom. The discrepancy function (which in this case is the likelihood ratio chi square statistic) is 2.761. Elsewhere in Amos output, the minimum value of the discrepancy function is referred to as **CMIN**. Here it is labeled **C** for brevity. To get an explanation of any column of the table, right-click anywhere in the column and select **What's This?** from the popup menu.

Notice that the best value in each column is underlined, except for the **Model** and **Notes** columns.

Many familiar fit measures (**CFI** and **RMSEA** for example) are omitted from this table. Appendix E gives a rationale for the choice of fit measures displayed.

## ❑ View some generated models

➜ You can double-click any row in the table (other than the **Sat** row) to see the corresponding path diagram in the Drawing Area. For example, double-click the row for Model 7 to see its path diagram:

*Figure 3: Model 7*

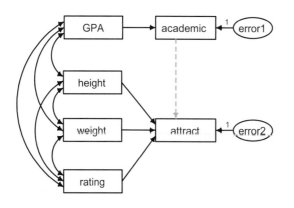

## ❑ View parameter estimates for a model

➔ Click 「γ」 on the **Specification Search** toolbar.

➔ In the **Specification Search** window, double-click the row for Model 7.

The Drawing Area displays the parameter estimates for Model 7, as seen in Figure 4:

*Figure 4: Parameter estimates for Model 7*

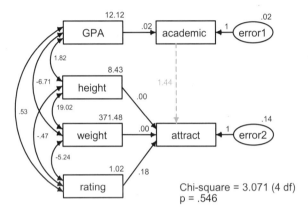

Chi-square = 3.071 (4 df)
p = .546

## ❑ Use BCC to compare models

➔ In the **Specification Search** window, click the column heading $BCC_0$.

The table then sorts according to **BCC** so that the best model according to **BCC** (i.e., the model with the smallest **BCC**) is at the top of the list.

| Model | Params | df | C | C-df | $BCC_0$ | $BIC_0$ | C / df | p | Notes |
|---|---|---|---|---|---|---|---|---|---|
| 7 | 17 | 4 | 3.071 | -0.929 | 0.000 | 0.000 | 0.768 | 0.546 | |
| 6 | 18 | 3 | 2.763 | -0.237 | 1.761 | 5.034 | 0.921 | 0.430 | |
| 8 | 18 | 3 | 2.895 | -0.105 | 1.894 | 5.167 | 0.965 | 0.408 | |
| 1 | 19 | 2 | 2.761 | 0.761 | 3.830 | 10.375 | 1.381 | 0.251 | |
| Sat | 21 | 0 | 0.000 | 0.000 | 5.208 | 18.299 | | | |
| 3 | 17 | 4 | 19.215 | 15.215 | 16.144 | 16.144 | 4.804 | 0.001 | |
| 2 | 18 | 3 | 19.155 | 16.155 | 18.154 | 21.427 | 6.385 | 0.000 | |
| 5 | 17 | 4 | 27.911 | 23.911 | 24.840 | 24.840 | 6.978 | 0.000 | |
| 4 | 16 | 5 | 67.342 | 62.342 | 62.201 | 58.929 | 13.468 | 0.000 | |

Following a suggestion by Burnham and Anderson (1998) a constant has been added to all the **BCC** values so that the smallest **BCC** value is zero. The "0" subscript on $BCC_0$ serves as a reminder of this rescaling. **AIC** (not shown in the above figure) and **BIC** have been similarly rescaled. As a rough guideline, Burnham and Anderson (1998, page 128) suggest the following interpretation of $AIC_0$. $BCC_0$ can be interpreted similarly.

*Table 1: Burnham and Anderson's guidelines for interpreting $AIC_0$ or $BCC_0$*

| $AIC_0$ or $BCC_0$ | Burnham and Anderson interpretation |
|---|---|
| $0 - 2$ | There is no credible evidence that the model should be ruled out as being the actual K-L best model for the population of possible samples. (See Burnham and Anderson for the definition of "K-L best".) |
| $2 - 4$ | There is weak evidence that the model is not the K-L best model. |
| $4 - 7$ | There is definite evidence that the model is not the K-L best model. |
| $7 - 10$ | There is strong evidence that the model is not the K-L best model. |
| $>10$ | There is very strong evidence that the model is not the K-L best model. |

Although Model 7 is estimated to be the best model, according to Burnham and Anderson's guidelines, Models 6 and 8 should not be ruled out.

## ❑ View the Akaike weights

➔ Click ☑ on the **Specification Search** toolbar.

➔ In the **Options** dialog box, click the **Current results** tab.

➔ In the **BCC, AIC, BIC** group, click **Akaike weights / Bayes factors (sum = 1)**.

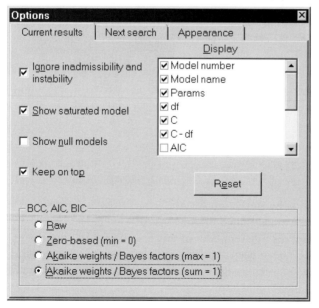

In the table of fit measures, the column that was labeled $BCC_0$ is now labeled $BCC_p$ and contains Akaike weights. (See Appendix G: Rescaling of AIC, BCC, and BIC.)

| Model | Params | df | C | C-df | BCCp | BICp | C / df | p | Notes |
|---|---|---|---|---|---|---|---|---|---|
| 7 | 17 | 4 | 3.071 | -0.929 | 0.494 | 0.860 | 0.768 | 0.546 | |
| 6 | 18 | 3 | 2.763 | -0.237 | 0.205 | 0.069 | 0.921 | 0.430 | |
| 8 | 18 | 3 | 2.895 | -0.105 | 0.192 | 0.065 | 0.965 | 0.408 | |
| 1 | 19 | 2 | 2.761 | 0.761 | 0.073 | 0.005 | 1.381 | 0.251 | |
| Sat | 21 | 0 | 0.000 | 0.000 | 0.037 | 0.000 | | | |
| 3 | 17 | 4 | 19.215 | 15.215 | 0.000 | 0.000 | 4.804 | 0.001 | |
| 2 | 18 | 3 | 19.155 | 16.155 | 0.000 | 0.000 | 6.385 | 0.000 | |
| 5 | 17 | 4 | 27.911 | 23.911 | 0.000 | 0.000 | 6.978 | 0.000 | |
| 4 | 16 | 5 | 67.342 | 62.342 | 0.000 | 0.000 | 13.468 | 0.000 | |

The Akaike weight has been interpreted (Akaike, 1978; Bozdogan, 1987; Burnham and Anderson, 1998) as the likelihood of the model given the data. With this interpretation, the estimated K-L best model (Model 7) is only about 2.4 times more likely (.494/.205 = 2.41) than Model 6. Bozdogan (1987) points out that, if it is possible to assign prior probabilities to the candidate models, the prior probabilities can be used together with the Akaike weights (interpreted as model likelihoods) to obtain posterior probabilities. With equal prior probabilities, the Akaike weights are themselves posterior probabilities, so that one can say that Model 7 is the K-L best model with probability .494, Model 6 is the K-L best model with probability .205, and so on. The four most probable models are Models 7, 6, 8 and 1. After adding their probabilities (.494 + .205 + .192 + .073 = .96) one can say that there is a 96% chance that the K-L best model is among those four. (Burnham and Anderson, 1998, pages 127-129). The "p" subscript on $BCC_p$ serves as a reminder that $BCC_p$ can be interpreted as a probability under some circumstances.

## ❑ Use BIC to compare models

➜ On the **Current results** tab of the **Options** dialog box, click **Zero-based (min = 0)** in the **BCC, AIC, BIC** group.

➜ In the **Specification Search** window, click the column heading **BIC₀**.

The table is now sorted according to **BIC**, so that the best model according to **BIC** (i.e., the model with the smallest **BIC**) is at the top of the list.

| Model | Params | df | C | C-df | $BCC_0$ | $BIC_0$ | C/df | p | Notes |
|-------|--------|----|--------|--------|---------|---------|--------|-------|-------|
| 7 | 17 | 4 | 3.071 | -0.929 | 0.000 | 0.000 | 0.768 | 0.546 | |
| 6 | 18 | 3 | 2.763 | -0.237 | 1.761 | 5.034 | 0.921 | 0.430 | |
| 8 | 18 | 3 | 2.895 | -0.105 | 1.894 | 5.167 | 0.965 | 0.408 | |
| 1 | 19 | 2 | 2.761 | 0.761 | 3.830 | 10.375 | 1.381 | 0.251 | |
| 3 | 17 | 4 | 19.215 | 15.215 | 16.144 | 16.144 | 4.804 | 0.001 | |
| Sat | 21 | 0 | 0.000 | 0.000 | 5.208 | 18.299 | | | |
| 2 | 18 | 3 | 19.155 | 16.155 | 18.154 | 21.427 | 6.385 | 0.000 | |
| 5 | 17 | 4 | 27.911 | 23.911 | 24.840 | 24.840 | 6.978 | 0.000 | |
| 4 | 16 | 5 | 67.342 | 62.342 | 62.201 | 58.929 | 13.468 | 0.000 | |

Model 7, with the smallest **BIC**, is the model with the highest posterior probability (approximately, using equal prior probabilities for the models and using a particular prior distribution for the parameters of each separate model). Raftery (1995) suggests the following interpretation of **BIC₀** values in judging the evidence for Model 7 against a competing model.

---

*Table 2 Raftery's (1995) guidelines for interpreting BIC$_0$*

| BIC$_0$ | Raftery (1995) interpretation |
|---------|-------------------------------|
| 0 – 2   | Weak                          |
| 2 – 6   | Positive                      |
| 6 – 10  | Strong                        |
| >10     | Very strong                   |

Using these guidelines there is "positive" evidence against Models 6 and 8, and "very strong" evidence against all other models as compared to Model 7.

## ❑ Use Bayes factors to compare models

➔ On the **Current results** tab of the **Options** dialog box, click **Akaike weights / Bayes factors (sum = 1)** in the **BCC, AIC, BIC** group.

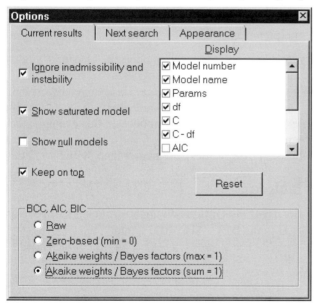

In the table of fit measures, the column that was labeled $BIC_0$ is now labeled $BIC_p$ and contains Bayes factors scaled so that they sum to 1.

| Model | Params | df | C | C - df | BCC$_p$ | BIC$_p$ | C / df | p | Notes |
|---|---|---|---|---|---|---|---|---|---|
| 7 | 17 | 4 | 3.071 | -0.929 | 0.494 | 0.860 | 0.768 | 0.546 | |
| 6 | 18 | 3 | 2.763 | -0.237 | 0.205 | 0.069 | 0.921 | 0.430 | |
| 8 | 18 | 3 | 2.895 | -0.105 | 0.192 | 0.065 | 0.965 | 0.408 | |
| 1 | 19 | 2 | 2.761 | 0.761 | 0.073 | 0.005 | 1.381 | 0.251 | |
| 3 | 17 | 4 | 19.215 | 15.215 | 0.000 | 0.000 | 4.804 | 0.001 | |
| Sat | 21 | 0 | 0.000 | 0.000 | 0.037 | 0.000 | | | |
| 2 | 18 | 3 | 19.155 | 16.155 | 0.000 | 0.000 | 6.385 | 0.000 | |
| 5 | 17 | 4 | 27.911 | 23.911 | 0.000 | 0.000 | 6.978 | 0.000 | |
| 4 | 16 | 5 | 67.342 | 62.342 | 0.000 | 0.000 | 13.468 | 0.000 | |

With equal prior probabilities for the models and using a particular prior distribution of the parameters of each separate model (Raftery, 1995; Schwarz, 1978), $BIC_p$ values are approximate posterior probabilities. Model 7 is the correct model with probability .860. One can be 99% sure that the correct model is among Models 7, 6, and 8 (.860 + .069 + .065 = .99). The "p" subscript is a reminder that $BIC_p$ values can be interpreted as probabilities.

Madigan and Raftery (1994) suggest that only models in "Occam's window" be used for purposes of model averaging (a topic not discussed here). The "symmetric" Occam's window is the subset of models obtained by excluding models that are much less probable (Madigan and Raftery suggest something like 20 times less probable) than the most probable model. In this example, the symmetric Occam's window contains models 7, 6 and 8 because these are the models whose probabilities ($BIC_p$ values) are greater than .860/20 = .043.

## ❑ Rescale the Bayes factors

➔ On the **Current results** tab of the **Options** dialog box, click **Akaike weights / Bayes factors (max = 1)** in the **BCC, AIC, BIC** group.

In the table of fit measures, the column that was labeled $BIC_p$ is now labeled $BIC_L$ and contains Bayes factors scaled so that the largest value is 1. This makes it easier to pick out Occam's window. It consists of models whose $BIC_L$ values are greater than $1/20 = .05$. In other words, Models 7, 6, and 8. The "L" subscript on $BIC_L$ is a reminder that the analogous statistic $BCC_L$ can be interpreted as a likelihood.

| Model | Params | df | C | C-df | $BCC_L$ | $BIC_L$ | C / df | p | Notes |
|-------|--------|----|--------|--------|---------|---------|--------|-------|-------|
| 7 | 17 | 4 | 3.071 | -0.929 | 1.000 | 1.000 | 0.768 | 0.546 | |
| 6 | 18 | 3 | 2.763 | -0.237 | 0.414 | 0.081 | 0.921 | 0.430 | |
| 8 | 18 | 3 | 2.895 | -0.105 | 0.388 | 0.076 | 0.965 | 0.408 | |
| 1 | 19 | 2 | 2.761 | 0.761 | 0.147 | 0.006 | 1.381 | 0.251 | |
| 3 | 17 | 4 | 19.215 | 15.215 | 0.000 | 0.000 | 4.804 | 0.001 | |
| Sat | 21 | 0 | 0.000 | 0.000 | 0.074 | 0.000 | | | |
| 2 | 18 | 3 | 19.155 | 16.155 | 0.000 | 0.000 | 6.385 | 0.000 | |
| 5 | 17 | 4 | 27.911 | 23.911 | 0.000 | 0.000 | 6.978 | 0.000 | |
| 4 | 16 | 5 | 67.342 | 62.342 | 0.000 | 0.000 | 13.468 | 0.000 | |

## ❑ Examine the short list of models

➔ Click ⬚ on the **Specification Search** toolbar. This displays a short list of models.

In Figure 5, the short list shows the best model for each number of parameters. It shows the best 16-parameter model, the best 17-parameter model, and so on. Notice that all criteria agree on the best model when the comparison is restricted to models with a fixed number of parameters. The overall best model must be on this list no matter which criterion is employed.

*Figure 5: The best model for each number of parameters*

| Model | Params | df | C | C - df | BCC$_L$ | BIC$_L$ | C / df | p | Notes |
|-------|--------|----|--------|--------|---------|---------|--------|-------|-------|
| 4 | 16 | 5 | 67.342 | 62.342 | 0.000 | 0.000 | 13.468 | 0.000 | |
| 7 | 17 | 4 | 3.071 | -0.929 | 1.000 | 1.000 | 0.768 | 0.546 | |
| 6 | 18 | 3 | 2.763 | -0.237 | 0.414 | 0.081 | 0.921 | 0.430 | |
| 1 | 19 | 2 | 2.761 | 0.761 | 0.147 | 0.006 | 1.381 | 0.251 | |
| Sat | 21 | 0 | 0.000 | 0.000 | 0.074 | 0.000 | | | |

This table shows that the best 17-parameter model fits substantially better than the best 16-parameter model. Beyond 17 parameters, adding additional parameters yields relatively small improvements in fit. In a cost-benefit analysis, stepping from 16 parameters to 17 parameters has a relatively large payoff while going beyond 17 parameters has a relatively small payoff. This suggests adopting the best 17-parameter using a heuristic "point of diminishing returns" argument. This approach to determining the number of parameters is pursued further later in this example (see **View the best fit graph for C**, page 32, and **View the scree plot for C**, page 34).

## ❑ View a scatterplot of fit and complexity

➔    Click 🖳 on the **Specification Search** toolbar. This opens the **Plot** window, which displays the following graph:

The graph shows a scatterplot of fit (measured by C) versus complexity (measured by number of parameters) where each point represents a model. The graph portrays the tradeoff between fit and complexity that Steiger characterized as follows:

> "In the final analysis, it may be, in a sense, impossible to define one *best* way to combine measures of complexity and measures of badness-of-fit in a single numerical index, because the precise nature of the *best* numerical tradeoff between complexity and fit is, to some extent, a matter of personal taste. The choice of a model is a classic problem in the two-dimensional analysis of preference." (Steiger, 1990, p. 179.)

→ Click any of the points in the scatterplot to display a menu that indicates which models are represented by that point and any overlapping points.

→ Choose one of the models from the popup menu to see that model highlighted in the table of model fit statistics, and at the same time to see the model's path diagram in the Drawing Area.

In the following figure, the cursor points to two overlapping points that represent models 6 (with a discrepancy of 2.76) and 8 (with a discrepancy of 2.90).

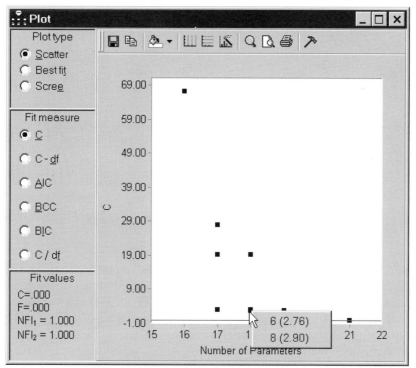

The graph contains a horizontal line representing points for which C is constant. Initially the line is centered at zero on the vertical axis. The **Fit values** panel at the lower left shows that for points on the horizontal line, C = 0 and also F = 0. (F is referred to as FMIN in Amos output.) $NFI_1$ and $NFI_2$ are two versions of NFI that use two different baseline models (see Appendix F: Baseline Models for Descriptive Fit Measures).

Initially, both $NFI_1$ and $NFI_2$ are equal to 1 for points on the horizontal line. The location of the horizontal line is adjustable. You can move the line by dragging it with the mouse. As you move the line you can see that changes in the location of the line are reflected in the fit measures in the lower left panel.

## ❑ Adjust the line representing constant fit

➔ Move the mouse pointer over the adjustable line. When the pointer changes into a hand, drag the line so that $NFI_1$ is equal to .900. (Keep an eye on $NFI_1$ in the lower left panel while you reposition the adjustable line.)

$NFI_1$ is the familiar form of the NFI statistic for which the baseline model requires the observed variables to be uncorrelated without constraining their means and variances. Points that are below the line have $(NFI_1) > .900$ and those above the line have $(NFI_1) < .900$. That is, the adjustable line separates the acceptable models from the unacceptable ones according to a widely used convention based on a remark by Bentler and Bonett (1980).

## ❑ View the line representing constant C-df

➜ In the **Plot** window, click **C-df** in the **Fit Measure** group. This displays the following graph:

The scatterplot remains unchanged except for the position of the adjustable line. The adjustable line now contains points for which **C-df** is constant. Whereas the line was previously horizontal, it is now tilted downward, indicating that **C-df** gives some weight to complexity in assessing model adequacy.

Initially, the adjustable line passes through the point for which **C-df** is smallest. Click that point, and then click Model 7 in the popup menu.

This highlights Model 7 in the table of fit measures and also displays Model 7's path diagram in the Drawing Area.

The panel in the lower left corner shows the value of some fit measures that depend only on **C-df** and that are therefore, like **C-df** itself, constant along the adjustable line. $CFI_1$ and $CFI_2$ are two versions of **CFI** that use two different baseline models (see Appendix G). Initially, both $CFI_1$ and $CFI_2$ are equal to 1 for points on the adjustable line. When you move the adjustable line, the fit measures in the lower left panel change to reflect the changing position of the line.

## ❑ Adjust the line representing constant C-df

➜ Using the mouse, drag the adjustable line so that $CFI_1$ is equal to .950.

$CFI_1$ is the usual **CFI** statistic for which the baseline model requires the observed variables to be uncorrelated without constraining their means and variances. Points that are below the line have $(CFI_1) > .950$ and those above the line have $(CFI_1) < .950$. That is, the adjustable line separates the acceptable models from the unacceptable ones according to the recommendation of Hu and Bentler (1999).

## ❑ View other lines representing constant fit

➜ Click **AIC, BCC,** and **BIC** in turn and notice that the adjustable line's slope becomes increasingly negative. This reflects the fact that the five measures, **C, C-df**, **AIC**, **BCC,** and **BIC**, give increasing weight to model complexity. For each of these five measures the adjustable line has constant slope, which you can confirm by dragging the line with the mouse. By contrast, the slope of the adjustable line for **C/df** is not constant—the line's slope changes when you drag it with the mouse—and so the slope for **C/df** cannot be compared to the slopes for **C, C-df**, **AIC**, **BCC, BIC,** and **BIC**.

---

## ❑ Explore the popup menus

➜ Right-click the graph at various locations and notice the menus that pop up. For example, if you right-click the title of the horizontal axis (**Number of Parameters**), the following menu appears:

You can use this menu to change the horizontal axis title as well as the title's color and font. Right-clicking elsewhere on the graph allows you to alter other features. For example, you can

- show or hide the toolbar

- change the background color

- edit the horizontal and vertical axis titles, as well as the title of the graph

- show or hide point labels

- change the font used for plot points and titles

- access the **Chart FX Properties** dialog box, which lets you choose formatting options such as the size and color of the dots that represent models, the thickness and color of lines (where applicable), and so on

## ❑ Explore the toolbar

If the toolbar is not already displayed, right-click the background of the **Plot** window and choose **Toolbar** from popup menu. If you hover the mouse over a button, a ToolTip appears that describes the its function. The toolbar buttons let you

- export the graph as a Chart FX file

- copy the graph to the Clipboard

- change the color of the background, points, and lines (choose a color from the palette, and then click and drag from the Color button to the part of the graph to which you want to apply the color)

- display a horizontal grid, vertical grid, or both

- access the **Chart FX Properties** dialog box

- adjust the zoom level

- display a print preview of the graph
- print the graph

## ❑ View the best fit graph for C

➔ In the **Plot** window, click **Best fit** in the **Plot type** group.

➔ In the **Fit measure** group, click **C**.

*Figure 6: Smallest value of C for each number of parameters*

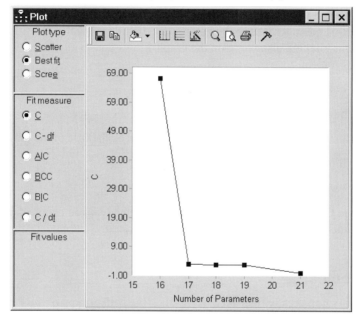

Each point in this graph represents a model for which C is less than or equal to that of any other model that has the same number of parameters. The graph shows that the best 16-parameter model has C = 67.342. The best 17-parameter model has C = 3.071. And so on. While **Best fit** is selected, the table of fit measures shows the best model for each number of parameters. This table appeared earlier as Figure 5.

| Model | Params | df | C | C - df | BCC$_L$ | BIC$_L$ | C / df | p | Notes |
|---|---|---|---|---|---|---|---|---|---|
| 4 | 16 | 5 | 67.342 | 62.342 | 0.000 | 0.000 | 13.468 | 0.000 | |
| 7 | 17 | 4 | 3.071 | -0.929 | 1.000 | 1.000 | 0.768 | 0.546 | |
| 6 | 18 | 3 | 2.763 | -0.237 | 0.414 | 0.081 | 0.921 | 0.430 | |
| 1 | 19 | 2 | 2.761 | 0.761 | 0.147 | 0.006 | 1.381 | 0.251 | |
| Sat | 21 | 0 | 0.000 | 0.000 | 0.074 | 0.000 | | | |

Notice that the best model for a fixed number of parameters does not depend on the choice of fit measure. For example, Model 7 is the best 17-parameter model

---

according to **C-df**, and also according to **C/df** and every other fit measure. This short list of best models is guaranteed to contain the overall best model no matter which fit measure is used as the criterion for model selection.

You can view the short list at any time by clicking [image icon]. The best fit graph suggests the choice of 17 as the "correct" number of parameters on the heuristic grounds that it is the "point of diminishing returns". That is, increasing the number of parameters from 16 to 17 "buys" a comparatively large improvement in C (67.342 - 3.071 = 64.271), while increasing the number of parameters beyond 17 yields relatively small improvements.

## ❑ View the best fit graph for other fit measures

➔ While **Best fit** is selected, try clicking the other choices in the **Fit measure** group: **C-df**, **AIC**, **BCC**, **BIC**, and **C/df**. For example, if you click **BIC**, you will see this:

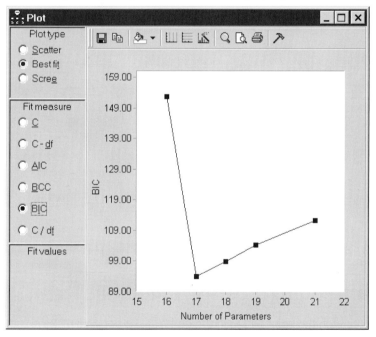

**BIC** is the measure among **C, C-df, AIC, BCC,** and **BIC** that imposes the greatest penalty for complexity. The high penalty for complexity is reflected in the steep positive slope of the graph as the number of parameters increases beyond 17. The graph makes it clear that, according to **BIC**, the best 17-parameter model is superior to any other candidate model.

Notice that clicking different fit measures changes the vertical axis of the best fit graph and changes the shape of the configuration of points.[1] However, the identity of each point is preserved. The best 16-parameter model is always Model 4, the best 17-parameter model is always Model 7, and so on. This is because, for a fixed number of parameters, the rank-order of models is the same for every fit measure.

## ❑ View the scree plot for C

➔ In the **Plot** window, click **Scree** in the **Plot Type** group.

➔ In the **Fit measure** group, click **C**.

The **Plot** window displays the following graph:

*Figure 7: Scree plot for C*

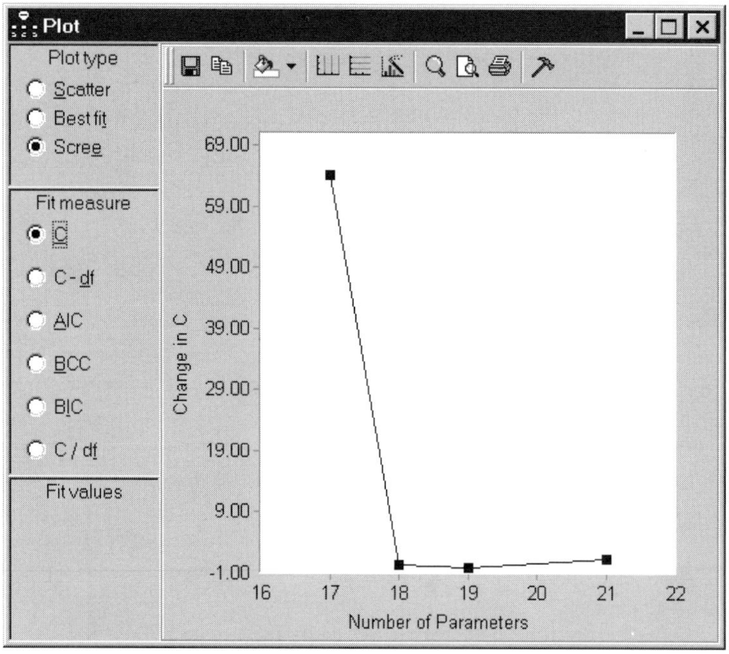

In this scree plot, the point with coordinate 17 on the horizontal axis has coordinate 64.271 on the vertical axis. This represents the fact that the best 17-parameter model (C = 3.071) fits better than the best 16-parameter model (C = 67.342), with the difference being 67.342 - 3.071 = 64.271. Similarly, the height of the graph at 18 parameters shows the improvement in C obtained by moving from the best 17-parameter model to the best 18-parameter model, and so on. The point located above 21 on the horizontal axis requires a separate explanation. There is no

---

[1] The saturated model is missing from the **C/df** graph because C/df is not defined for the saturated model.

20-parameter model with which the best 21-parameter model can be compared. (Actually there is only one 21-parameter model—the saturated model.) The best 21-parameter model (C = 0) is therefore compared to the best 19-parameter model (C = 2.761). The height of the 21-parameter point is calculated as (2.761 – 0)/2. That is, the improvement in C obtained by moving from the 19-parameter model to the 21-parameter model is expressed as the amount of reduction in C *per parameter*.

Either Figure 6 or Figure 7 can be used to support a heuristic "point of diminishing returns" argument in favor of 17 parameters. There is this difference: in the best fit graph (Figure 6), one looks for an "elbow" in the graph, or a place where the slope changes from relatively steep to relatively flat. For the present problem, this occurs at 17 parameters, which can be taken as support for the best 17-parameter model. In the scree plot (Figure 7), one also looks for an elbow, but the elbow occurs at 18 parameters in this example. This is also taken as support for the best 17-parameter model. In a scree plot an elbow at *k* parameters provides support for the best (*k*-1)-parameter model.

The scree plot is so named because of its similarity to the graph known as a scree plot in principal components analysis (Cattell, 1966). In principal components analysis, a scree plot shows the improvement in model fit that is obtained by adding components to the model, one component at a time. The scree plot presented here for SEM shows the improvement in model fit that is obtained by incrementing the number of model parameters. The scree plot for SEM is not identical in all respects to the scree plot for principal components analysis. For example, in principal components one obtains a sequence of nested models when introducing components one at a time. This is not necessarily the case in the scree plot for SEM. The best 17-parameter model, say, and the best 18-parameter model may or may not be nested. (In the present example, they are.) Furthermore, in principal components, the scree plot is always monotone non-increasing, which is not guaranteed in the case of the scree plot for SEM, even with nested models. Indeed, the scree plot for the present example is not monotone.

In spite of the differences between the traditional scree plot and the scree plot presented here, it is proposed that the new scree plot be used in the same heuristic fashion as the traditional one. A two-stage approach to model selection is suggested. In the first stage, the number of parameters is selected by examining either the scree plot or the short list of models. In the second stage, the best model is chosen from among those models that have the number of parameters determined in the first stage.

## ❑ View the scree plot for other fit measures

➔ With **Scree** selected in the **Plot Type** group, click the other choices in the **Fit measure** group: **C-df**, **AIC**, **BCC**, and **BIC** (but not **C/df**).

For example, if you click **BIC**, you will see this:

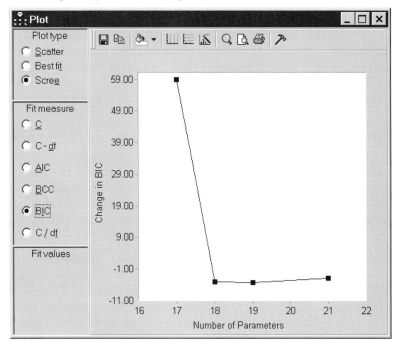

For **C-df**, **AIC**, **BCC**, and **BIC**, the units and the origin of the vertical axis are different than for **C**, but the graphs are otherwise identical. This means that the final model selected by the scree test is independent of which measure of fit is used (unless **C/df** is used). This is the advantage of the scree plot over the "best fit" plot demonstrated earlier in this example (see **View the best fit graph for C**, page 32, and **View the best fit graph for other fit measures**, page 33). The best fit plot and the scree plot contain nearly the same information, but the shape of the best fit plot depends on the choice of fit measure while the shape of the scree plot does not (with the exception of **C/df**).

Both the best fit plot and the scree plot are independent of sample size in the sense that altering the sample size without altering the sample moments has no effect other than to rescale the vertical axis.

## Specification search with many optional arrows

The previous specification search was largely confirmatory in that there were only three optional arrows. You can take a much more exploratory approach to constructing a model for the Felson and Bohrnstedt data.

Suppose that your only hypothesis about the six measured variables is that

(1) **academic** depends on the other five variables, and

(2) **attract** depends on the other five variables.

The path diagram in Figure 8 with 11 optional arrows implements this hypothesis. It specifies which variables are endogenous, and nothing more. Every observed-variable model that is consistent with the hypothesis is included in the specification search. The covariances among the observed, exogenous variables could have been made optional, but doing so would have increased the number of optional arrows from 11 to 17, increasing the number of candidate models from 2,048 (i.e., $2^{11}$) to 131,072 (i.e., $2^{17}$). Allowing the covariances among the observed, exogenous variables to be optional thus would have been costly, and there would seem to be little interest in searching for models in which some pairs of those variables are uncorrelated.

*Figure 8: Highly exploratory model for Felson and Bohrnstedt's girls' data*

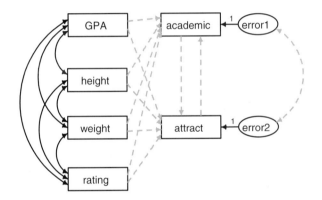

## ❑ Specify the model

➔ Choose **File→Open** from the Amos Graphics menu bar.

➔ In the **Open** dialog box, double-click the file **Ex22b.amw**. If you performed a typical installation, the path will be
**C:\Program Files\Amos 5\Examples\Ex22b.amw**.

**Tip:** If the last file you opened was in the Examples folder, you can open the file by double-clicking it in the Files list to the left of the Drawing Area.

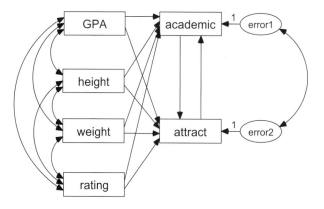

## ❑ Open the Specification Search window

➜ Click 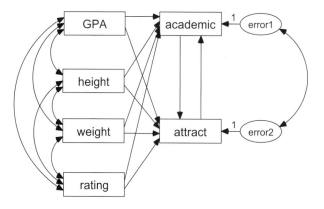 on the Amos Graphics toolbar, or choose **Model-Fit→Specification Search** from the menu bar.

## ❑ Make some arrows optional

➜ Click on the **Specification Search** toolbar, and then click the arrows in the path diagram until it looks like Figure 8.

**Tip:** You can change multiple arrows at once by clicking and dragging the mouse pointer through them.

## ❑ Set options to their defaults

➜ Click on the **Specification Search** toolbar.

➜ In the **Options** dialog box, click the **Next search** tab.

➜ In the **Retain only the best ___ models** number box, change the value from **0** to **10**.

Current results | Next search | Appearance

2,048 models will be fitted

⊙ All subsets          ○ Stepwise

○ Forward             ○ Backward

[  0 ⬍] Use no more than ___ optional parameters.

[ 10 ⬍] Retain only the best ___ models.

Benchmark models
   ☑ Saturated
   ☑ Null 1
   ☑ Null 2
   ☑ Null 3
   ☑ Null 4

This restores the default setting we altered earlier in this example. With the default setting, the program displays only the ten best models according to whichever criterion you use for sorting the columns of the model list. This limitation is desirable now because of the large number of models that will be generated for this specification search.

➔  Now click the **Current results** tab.

➔  In the **BCC, AIC, BIC** group, click **Zero-based (min = 0)**.

## ❑ Perform the specification search

➔  Click ▶ on the **Specification Search** toolbar. The search takes about ten seconds on a 1.8 Ghz Pentium 4. When it finishes, the **Specification Search** window expands to show the results.

## ❑ Use BIC to compare models

➔  In the **Specification Search** window, click the $BIC_0$ column heading. This sorts the table according to $BIC_0$.

*Figure 9: The ten best models according to $BIC_0$*

| Model | Params | df | C | C-df | $BCC_0$ | $BIC_0$ | C/df | p | Notes |
|---|---|---|---|---|---|---|---|---|---|
| 22 | 15 | 6 | 5.156 | -0.844 | 0.132 | 0.000 | 0.859 | 0.524 | |
| 32 | 16 | 5 | 2.954 | -2.046 | 0.000 | 3.141 | 0.591 | 0.707 | |
| 33 | 16 | 5 | 3.101 | -1.899 | 0.147 | 3.288 | 0.620 | 0.684 | |
| 34 | 16 | 5 | 4.623 | -0.377 | 1.669 | 4.810 | 0.925 | 0.464 | |
| 35 | 16 | 5 | 4.623 | -0.377 | 1.669 | 4.810 | 0.925 | 0.464 | |
| 36 | 16 | 5 | 4.623 | -0.377 | 1.669 | 4.810 | 0.925 | 0.464 | |
| 37 | 16 | 5 | 5.055 | 0.055 | 2.101 | 5.242 | 1.011 | 0.409 | Unstable |
| 38 | 16 | 5 | 5.055 | 0.055 | 2.101 | 5.242 | 1.011 | 0.409 | |
| 39 | 16 | 5 | 5.079 | 0.079 | 2.125 | 5.266 | 1.016 | 0.406 | |
| 40 | 16 | 5 | 5.081 | 0.081 | 2.127 | 5.268 | 1.016 | 0.406 | |

The sorted table shows that Model 22 is the best model according to **$BIC_0$.** (Model numbers depend in part on the order in which the objects in the path diagram were drawn, so if you draw your own path diagram your model numbers may differ from the model numbers here.) The second-best model according to **$BIC_0$**, namely Model 32, is the best according to **$BCC_0$.** These models are shown in Figure 10.

*Figure 10: Models 22 and 32*

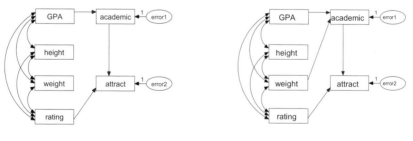

Model 22                      Model 32

## ❑ View the scree plot

→ Click 🖻 on the **Specification Search** toolbar.

→ In the **Plot** window, click **Scree** in the **Plot Type** group.

The scree plot strongly suggests that models with 15 parameters provide an optimum tradeoff of model fit and parsimony.

→ Click the point with the horizontal coordinate 15. A menu appears that indicates the point represents Model 22, which has a chi square value of 46.22.

➔ On the popup menu, click **22 (46.22)**. This displays Model 22 in the Drawing Area (see Figure 10).

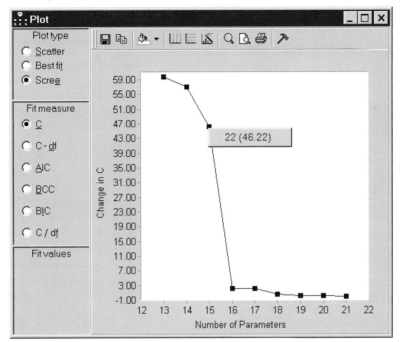

## Limitations

The specification search procedure is limited to the analysis of data from a single group.

# Example 23: Exploratory Factor Analysis by Specification Search

## Purpose

- Demonstrate exploratory factor analysis by means of a specification search. In this approach to exploratory factor analysis, any measured variable can (optionally) depend on any factor. A specification search is performed to find the subset of single-headed arrows that provides the optimum combination of simplicity and fit.

- Demonstrate a heuristic specification search that is practical for models that are too big for an exhaustive specification search.

## The data

This example uses the Holzinger and Swineford girls' (1939) data from Example 8.

## The model

The initial model is shown in Figure 11. During the specification search, all single-headed arrows that point from factors to measured variables will be made optional. The purpose of the specification search is to obtain guidance as to which single-headed arrows are essential to the model—in other words, which variables depend on which factors.

The two factor variances are both fixed at 1 in Figure 11, as are all the regression weights associated with residual variables. Without these constraints, all the models encountered during the specification search would be unidentified.

*Figure 11: Exploratory factor analysis model with two factors*

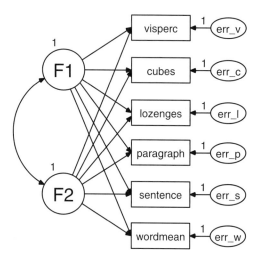

## ❑ Specify the model

➔ Choose **File→Open** from the Amos Graphics menu bar.

➔ In the **Open** dialog box, double-click the file **Ex23.amw**. If you performed a typical installation, the path will be **C:\Program Files\Amos 5\Examples\Ex23.amw**.

**Tip:** If the last file you opened was in the Examples folder, you can open the file by double-clicking it in the Files list to the left of the Drawing Area.

Initially, the path diagram appears as in Figure 11. There is no point in trying to fit this model as it stands because it is not identified, even with the factor variances fixed at 1.

## ❑ Open the Specification Search window

➔ Click 🔍 on the Amos Graphics toolbar, or choose **Model-Fit→Specification Search** from the menu bar.

This opens the **Specification Search** window. Initially, only the toolbar is visible, as seen here:

## ❑ Make all the regression weights optional

➜ Click ⬚ on the **Specification Search** toolbar, and then click all the single-headed arrows in the path diagram.

**Tips:**

- You can change multiple arrows at once by clicking and dragging the mouse pointer through them.

- If you want the optional arrows to appear as dashed as well as colored, as seen in the following figure, choose **View/Set→Interface Properties** from the Amos Graphic menu bar, and then on the **Accessibility** tab, select the **Alternative to color** checkbox.

*Figure 12: Two factor model with all regression weights optional*

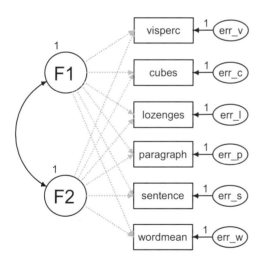

During the specification search the program will attempt to fit the model using every possible subset of the optional arrows.

## ☐ Set options to their defaults

➔ Click ☑ on the **Specification Search** toolbar.

➔ In the **Options** dialog box, click the **Current results** tab.

➔ Click **Reset** to ensure that your options are the same as those used in this example.

```
┌─ Options ──────────────────────────────────────── ⊠ ┐
│  Current results  │  Next search  │  Appearance  │    │
│                                   Display            │
│   ☑ Ignore inadmissibility and   ☑ Model number ▲   │
│      instability                 ☑ Model name        │
│                                  ☑ Params            │
│   ☑ Show saturated model         ☑ df               │
│                                  ☑ C                 │
│                                  ☑ C - df            │
│   ☐ Show null models             ☐ AIC          ▼   │
│                                                      │
│   ☑ Keep on top                                      │
│                                  ┌──────────────┐    │
│                                  │    Reset     │    │
│                                  └──────────────┘    │
│  ┌─ BCC, AIC, BIC ─────────────────────────────┐    │
│  │  ○ Raw                                        │    │
│  │  ⦿ Zero-based (min = 0)                       │    │
│  │  ○ Akaike weights / Bayes factors (max = 1)  │    │
│  │  ○ Akaike weights / Bayes factors (sum = 1)  │    │
│  └──────────────────────────────────────────────┘   │
└──────────────────────────────────────────────────────┘
```

➔ Now click the **Next search** tab. Notice that the default value for **Retain only the best ___ models** is **10**.

```
┌─ Options ──────────────────────────────────────── ⊠ ┐
│  Current results  │  Next search  │  Appearance  │    │
│           1 model will be fitted                     │
│                                                      │
│      ⦿ All subsets          ○ Stepwise              │
│                                                      │
│      ○ Forward              ○ Backward              │
│                                                      │
│                                                      │
│    ┌── 0 ┈┐ Use no more than ___ optional parameters.│
│    ┌── 10 ┈┐ Retain only the best ___ models.       │
│                                                      │
│  Benchmark models                                    │
│              ☑ Saturated                             │
│              ☑ Null 1                                │
│              ☑ Null 2                                │
│              ☑ Null 3                                │
│              ☑ Null 4                                │
└──────────────────────────────────────────────────────┘
```

With this setting, the program will display only the ten best models according to whichever criterion you use for sorting the columns of the model list. For example, if you click the column heading **C/df**, the table will show the ten models with the smallest values of **C/df**, sorted according to **C/df**. Scatterplots will display only the ten best 1-parameter models, the ten best 2-parameter models, and so on. It is useful to place a limit on the number of parameters to be displayed when there are a lot of optional parameters. In this example there are 12 optional parameters so that there are $2^{12} = 4096$ candidate models. Storing results for a large number of models can affect performance. Limiting the display to the best ten models for each number of parameters means that the program only has to maintain a list of about $10 \times 13 = 130$ models. The program will have to fit many more than 130 models in order to find the best ten models for each number of parameters, but not quite as many as 4096. The program uses a branch and bound algorithm similar to the one used in all-possible-subsets regression (Furnival and Wilson, 1974) to avoid fitting some models unnecessarily.

## ❑ Perform the specification search

➔ Click ▶ on the **Specification Search** toolbar. The search takes about 12 seconds on a 1.8 Ghz Pentium 4. When it finishes, the **Specification Search** window expands to show the results.

The list of models is initially not very informative. The models are listed in the order in which they were encountered, and the models encountered early in the search were found to be unidentified. The method used for classifying models as unidentified is described in Appendix D.

| Model | Params | df | C | C - df | $BCC_0$ | $BIC_0$ | C / df | p | Notes |
|-------|--------|----|---|--------|---------|---------|--------|---|-------|
| 1 | 7 | 14 | | | | | | | Unidentified |
| 2 | 8 | 13 | | | | | | | Unidentified |
| 3 | 8 | 13 | | | | | | | Unidentified |
| 4 | 8 | 13 | | | | | | | Unidentified |
| 5 | 8 | 13 | | | | | | | Unidentified |
| 6 | 8 | 13 | | | | | | | Unidentified |
| 7 | 8 | 13 | | | | | | | Unidentified |
| 8 | 8 | 13 | | | | | | | Unidentified |
| 9 | 8 | 13 | | | | | | | Unidentified |
| 10 | 8 | 13 | | | | | | | Unidentified |

## ❑ Use BCC to compare models

➔ In the **Specification Search** window, click the column heading $BCC_0$.

The table then sorts according to **BCC** so that the best model according to **BCC** (i.e., the model with the smallest **BCC**) is at the top of the list.

*Figure 13: The 10 best models according to BCC$_0$*

| Model | Params | df | C | C-df | BCC$_0$ | BIC$_0$ | C/df | p | Notes |
|---|---|---|---|---|---|---|---|---|---|
| 52 | 13 | 8 | 7.853 | -0.147 | 0.000 | 0.000 | 0.982 | 0.448 | |
| 53 | 13 | 8 | 7.853 | -0.147 | 0.000 | 0.000 | 0.982 | 0.448 | |
| 62 | 14 | 7 | 5.770 | -1.230 | 0.132 | 2.207 | 0.824 | 0.567 | |
| 63 | 14 | 7 | 5.770 | -1.230 | 0.132 | 2.207 | 0.824 | 0.567 | |
| 65 | 14 | 7 | 7.155 | 0.155 | 1.517 | 3.593 | 1.022 | 0.413 | |
| 64 | 14 | 7 | 7.155 | 0.155 | 1.517 | 3.593 | 1.022 | 0.413 | |
| 67 | 14 | 7 | 7.608 | 0.608 | 1.971 | 4.046 | 1.087 | 0.368 | |
| 66 | 14 | 7 | 7.608 | 0.608 | 1.971 | 4.046 | 1.087 | 0.368 | |
| 68 | 14 | 7 | 7.632 | 0.632 | 1.995 | 4.070 | 1.090 | 0.366 | |
| 69 | 14 | 7 | 7.632 | 0.632 | 1.995 | 4.070 | 1.090 | 0.366 | |

The two best models according to **BCC$_0$** (Models 52 and 53) have identical fit measures (out to 3 decimal places anyway). The explanation for this can be seen from the path diagrams for the two models.

➔ In the **Specification Search** window, double-click the row for Model 52. This displays its path diagram in the Drawing Area.

➔ To see the path diagram for Model 53, double-click its row.

*Figure 14: Reversing F1 and F2 yields another candidate model*

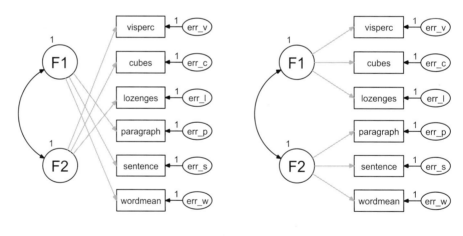

**Model 52**            **Model 53**

This is just one pair of models where reversing the roles of **F1** and **F2** changes one member of the pair into the other. There are other such pairs. Models 52 and 53 are equivalent although they are counted separately in the list of 4096 candidate models. The ten models in Figure 13 come in five pairs, but candidate models do not always come in equivalent pairs, as Figure 15 illustrates. The model in Figure 15 does not occur among the ten best models for six optional parameters, and is not identified for that matter, but it does illustrate how reversing **F1** and **F2** can fail to yield a different member of the set of 4096 candidate models.

*Figure 15: Reversing F1 and F2 yields the same candidate model*

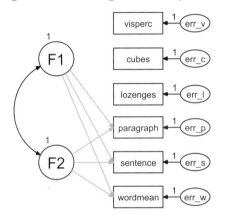

The occurrence of equivalent candidate models makes it unclear how to apply Bayesian calculations to select a model in this example. Similarly it is unclear how to use Akaike weights. Furthermore, Burnham and Anderson's guidelines (see page 20) for the interpretation of $BCC_0$ are based on reasoning about Akaike weights, so it is not clear whether those guidelines apply in the present example. On the other hand the use of $BCC_0$ without reference to the Burnham and Anderson guidelines seems unexceptionable. Model 52 (or the equivalent Model 53) is the best model according to $BCC_0$.

Although **BCC₀** chooses the model employed in Example 8, which was based on a model of Jöreskog and Sörbom (1996), it might be noted that Model 62 (or its equivalent, Model 63) is a very close second in terms of **BCC₀** and is the best model according to some other fit measures. Model 63 has the following path diagram:

*Figure 16: Model 63*

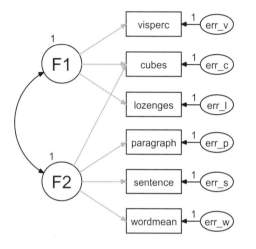

The factors, **F1** and **F2**, seem roughly interpretable as **spatial ability** and **verbal ability** in both Models 53 and 63. The two models differ in their explanation of scores on the **cubes** test. In Model 53 cubes scores depend entirely on **spatial ability**. In Model 63, **cubes** scores depend on both **spatial ability** and **verbal ability**. Since it is a close call in terms of every criterion based on fit and parsimony, it may be especially appropriate here to pay attention to interpretability as a model selection criterion. The scree test in the following step, however, does not equivocate as to which is the best model.

## ❑ View the scree plot

➜   Click ▨ on the **Specification Search** toolbar.

➜   In the **Plot** window, click **Scree** in the **Plot Type** group.

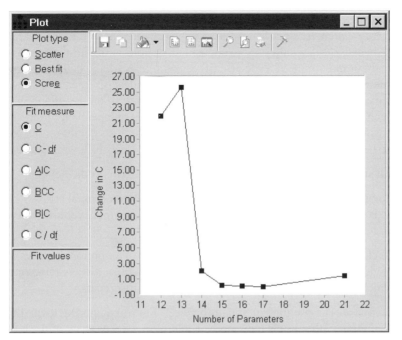

The scree plot strongly suggests the use of 13 parameters because of the way the graph drops abruptly and then levels off immediately after the 13th parameter. Click the point with coordinate 13 on the horizontal axis. A popup menu shows that the point represents Models 52 and 53 shown in Figure 14.

## ❑ View the short list of models

➔ Click ⊞ on the **Specification Search** toolbar. Take note of the short list of models for future reference.

# Heuristic specification search

The number of models that must be fitted in an exhaustive specification search grows rapidly with the number of optional arrows. There are 12 optional arrows in Figure 12 so that an exhaustive specification search requires fitting $2^{12} = 4096$ models. (The number of models will be somewhat smaller if you specify a small positive number for **Retain only the best___models** on the **Next search** tab of the **Options** dialog box.) A number of heuristic search procedures have been proposed for reducing the number of models that have to be fitted (Salhi, 1998). None of these is guaranteed to find the best model, but they have the advantage of being computationally feasible in problems with more than, say, 20 optional arrows where an exhaustive specification search is impossible.

---

Amos provides three heuristic search strategies in addition to the option of an exhaustive search. The heuristic strategies do not attempt to find the overall best model, because this would require choosing a definition of "best" in terms of the minimum or maximum of a specific fit measure. Instead, the heuristic strategies attempt to find the 1-parameter model with the smallest discrepancy, the 2-parameter model with the smallest discrepancy, and so on. By adopting this approach, a search procedure can be designed that is independent of the choice of fit measure. You can select among the available search strategies on the **Next search** tab of the **Options** dialog box. The choices are as follows:

- **All subsets**. An exhaustive search is performed. This is the default.

- **Forward**. The program first fits the model with no optional arrows. Then it adds one optional arrow at a time, always adding whichever arrow gives the largest reduction in discrepancy.

- **Backward**. The program first fits the model with all optional arrows in the model. Then it removes one optional arrow at a time, always removing whichever arrow gives the smallest increase in discrepancy.

- **Stepwise**. The program alternates between **Forward** and **Backward** searches, beginning with a **Forward** search. The program keeps track of the best 1-optional-arrow model encountered, the best 2-optional-arrow model, and so on. After the first **Forward** search, the **Forward** and **Backward** search algorithms are modified by the following rule: The program will add an arrow or remove an arrow only if the resulting model has a smaller discrepancy than any previously encountered model with the same number of arrows. For example, the program will add an arrow to a 5-optional-arrow model only if the resulting 6-optional-arrow model has a smaller discrepancy than any previously encountered 6-optional-arrow model. **Forward** and **Backward** searches are alternated until one **Forward** or **Backward** search is completed with no improvement.

## ❑ Perform a stepwise search

➔ Click ☑ on the **Specification Search** toolbar.

➔ In the **Options** dialog box, click the **Next search** tab.

➔ Click **Stepwise**.

➔ On the **Specification Search** toolbar, click ▶.

The results in Figure 17 suggest examining the 13-parameter model, Model 7. Its discrepancy C is much smaller than the discrepancy for the best 12-parameter model and not much larger than the best 14-parameter model. Model 7 is also best according to both **BCC** and **BIC**. (Your results may differ from those in Figure 17 because of an element of randomness in the heuristic specification search algorithms. When adding an arrow during a forward step or removing an arrow during a backward step, there may not be a unique best choice. In that case, one arrow is picked at random from among the arrows that are tied for best.)

*Figure 17: Results of stepwise specification search*

| Model | Params | df | C | C - df | $BCC_0$ | $BIC_0$ | C / df | p | Notes |
|-------|--------|-----|--------|--------|---------|---------|--------|-------|-------------|
| 1 | 7 | 14 | | | | | | | Unidentified |
| 2 | 8 | 13 | | | | | | | Unidentified |
| 3 | 9 | 12 | | | | | | | Unidentified |
| 4 | 10 | 11 | | | | | | | Unidentified |
| 5 | 11 | 10 | 97.475 | 87.475 | 85.191 | 81.041 | 9.747 | 0.000 | |
| 6 | 12 | 9 | 33.469 | 24.469 | 23.401 | 21.326 | 3.719 | 0.000 | |
| 7 | 13 | 8 | 7.853 | -0.147 | 0.000 | 0.000 | 0.982 | 0.448 | |
| 8 | 14 | 7 | 5.770 | -1.230 | 0.132 | 2.207 | 0.824 | 0.567 | |
| 9 | 15 | 6 | 5.594 | -0.406 | 2.172 | 6.322 | 0.932 | 0.470 | |
| 10 | 16 | 5 | 5.528 | 0.528 | 4.322 | 10.547 | 1.106 | 0.355 | |
| 11 | 17 | 4 | 5.476 | 1.476 | 6.485 | 14.785 | 1.369 | 0.242 | |
| 12 | 18 | 3 | | | | | | | Unidentified |
| 13 | 19 | 2 | | | | | | | Unidentified |
| Sat | 21 | 0 | 0.000 | 0.000 | 9.870 | 26.471 | | | |

## ❑ View the scree plot

➔ Click ▨ on the **Specification Search** toolbar.

➔ In the **Plot** window, click **Scree** in the **Plot Type** group.

The scree plot confirms that adding a $13^{th}$ parameter provides a substantial reduction in discrepancy and that adding additional parameters beyond the $13^{th}$ provides only slight reductions.

*Figure 18: Scree plot after stepwise specification search*

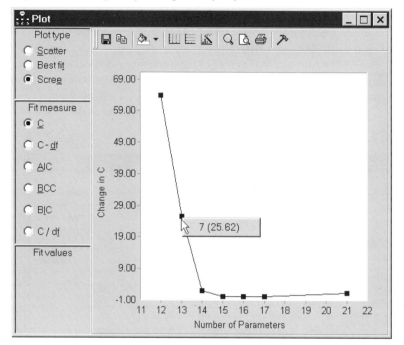

➔  Click the point in the scree plot with horizontal coordinate 13, as shown in Figure 18. The popup menu that appears shows that Model 7 is the best 13-parameter model.

➔  On the popup menu, click **7 (25.62)**. This displays the path diagram for Model 7 in the Drawing Area.

**Tip:** You can also do this by double-clicking the row for Model 7 in the **Specification Search** window.

## Limitations of heuristic specification searches

A heuristic specification search can fail to find any of the best models for a given number of parameters. In fact, the stepwise search in the present example did fail to find any of the best 11-parameter models. As Figure 17 shows, the best 11-parameter model found by the stepwise search had a discrepancy (C) of 97.475. An exhaustive search, however, turns up two models that have a discrepancy of 55.382. For every other number of parameters, the stepwise search did find one of the best models.

Of course it is only when you can perform an exhaustive search to double-check the result of a heuristic search that you can know whether the heuristic search was successful. In those problems where a heuristic search is the only available technique, not only is there no guarantee that it will find one of the best models for each number of parameters, but there is no way to know whether it has succeeded in doing so.

Even in those cases where a heuristic search finds one of the best models for a given number of parameters, it does not (as implemented in Amos) give information about other models that fit equally well or nearly as well.

# Example 24: Multiple-Group Factor Analysis

---

## Purpose

- Demonstrate a two-group factor analysis with automatic specification of cross-group constraints.

---

## Introduction

This example demonstrates Amos's automatically generated cross-group constraints for a two-group factor analysis model.

---

## The data

This example uses the Holzinger and Swineford girls' and boys' (1939) data from Examples 12 and 15.

---

## Model 24a: Modeling without means and intercepts

The presence of means and intercepts as explicit model parameters adds to the complexity of a multiple-group analysis. The treatment of means and intercepts will be postponed until Model 24b. For now, consider fitting the following factor analysis model, with no explicit means and intercepts, to the data of girls and also boys.

---

*Figure 19: Two-factor model for girls and boys*

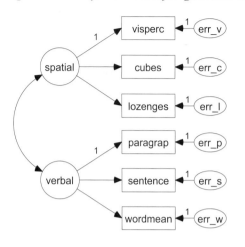

This is the same two-group factor analysis problem that was considered in Example 12. The results obtained in Example 12 will be obtained here automatically.

## ❑ Specify the model

➜ Choose **File→Open** from the Amos Graphics menu bar.

➜ In the **Open** dialog box, double-click the file **Ex24a.amw**. If you performed a typical installation, the path will be **C:\Program Files\Amos 5\Examples\Ex24a.amw**.

**Tip:** If the last file you opened was in the Examples folder, you can open the file by double-clicking it in the Files list to the left of the Drawing Area.

The path diagram is the same for boys as for girls, and is shown in Figure 19. Some regression weights are fixed at 1. These regression weights will remain fixed at 1 throughout the analysis to follow. The assisted multiple-group analysis adds constraints to the model you specify, but does not remove any constraints.

## ❑ Open the Multiple-Group Analysis dialog box

➜ Click 📇 on the Amos Graphics toolbar, or choose **Model-Fit→Multiple-Group Analysis** from the menu bar.

➜ Click **OK** in the message box that appears. This opens the **Multiple-Group Analysis** dialog box.

*Figure 20: The Multiple-Group Analysis dialog box*

| Multiple-Group Analysis | | | | | | | | |
|---|---|---|---|---|---|---|---|---|
| Parameter Subsets | | | | Models | | | | |
| | 1 | 2 | 3 | 4 | 5 | 6 | 7 | 8 |
| Measurement weights | ☑ | ☑ | ☑ | ☐ | ☐ | ☐ | ☐ | ☐ |
| Measurement intercepts | ☐ | ☑ | ☑ | ☐ | ☐ | ☐ | ☐ | ☐ |
| Structural weights | ☐ | ☑ | ☑ | ☐ | ☐ | ☐ | ☐ | ☐ |
| Structural intercepts | ☐ | ☑ | ☑ | ☐ | ☐ | ☐ | ☐ | ☐ |
| Structural means | ☐ | ☑ | ☑ | ☐ | ☐ | ☐ | ☐ | ☐ |
| Structural covariances | ☐ | ☑ | ☑ | ☐ | ☐ | ☐ | ☐ | ☐ |
| Structural residuals | ☐ | ☐ | ☑ | ☐ | ☐ | ☐ | ☐ | ☐ |
| Measurement residuals | ☐ | ☐ | ☑ | ☐ | ☐ | ☐ | ☐ | ☐ |

| Help | Default | OK | Cancel |
|---|---|---|---|

Most of the time, you will simply click **OK**. This time, however, let's take a look at some parts of the **Multiple-Group Analysis** dialog box.

There are eight columns of checkboxes. Check marks appear only in the columns labeled **1**, **2** and **3**. This means that the program will generate three models, each with a different set of cross-group constraints.

Column 1 contains a single check mark in the row labeled **Measurement weights**, which is short for "regression weights in the measurement part of the model". In the case of a factor analysis model, these are the "factor loadings". The following section shows you how to view the measurement weights in the path diagram. Column 1 generates a model in which measurement weights are constant across groups (i.e., the same for boys as for girls).

Column 2 contains check marks for **Measurement weights** and also **Structural covariances**, which is short for "variances and covariances in the structural part of the model". In a factor analysis model, these are the factor variances and covariances. The following section shows you how to view the structural covariances in the path diagram. Column 2 generates a model in which measurement weights and structural covariances are constant across groups.

Column 3 contains all the check marks in column 2, and also a check mark next to **Measurement residuals**, which is short for "variances and covariances of residual (error) variables in the measurement part of the model". The following section shows you how to view the measurement residuals in the path diagram. The three parameter subsets that appear in a black (i.e., not gray) font are mutually exclusive and exhaustive, so that column 3 generates a model in which all parameters are constant across groups.

---

In summary, columns 1 through 3 generate a hierarchy of models in which each model contains all the constraints of its predecessor. First the "factor loadings" are held constant across groups. Then the factor variances and covariances are held constant. Finally, the residual (unique) variances are held constant.

## ❑ View the parameter subsets

➜ In the **Multiple-Group Analysis** dialog box, click **Measurement weights**.

The measurement weights are now displayed in color in the Drawing Area. If you changed the accessibility options (see page 5), they also display as thick lines, as shown here:

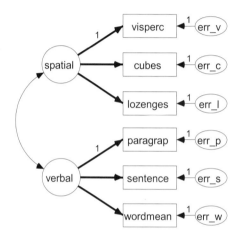

➜ Click **Structural covariances** to see the factor variances and covariances emphasized.

➜ Click **Measurement residuals** to see the error variables emphasized.

This is an easy way to visualize which parameters are affected by each cross-group constraint.

## ❑ View the generated models

➜ In the **Multiple-Group Analysis** dialog box, click **OK**.

The path diagram now shows names for all parameters. In the panel at the left of the path diagram, you can see that the program has generated three new models in addition to an **Unconstrained** model in which there are no cross-group constraints at all.

*Figure 21: Amos Graphics window after automatic constraints*

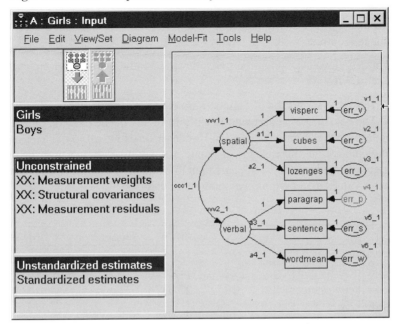

→ Double-click **XX: Measurement weights**. This opens the **Manage Models** dialog box, which shows you the constraints that require the "factor loadings" to be constant across groups.

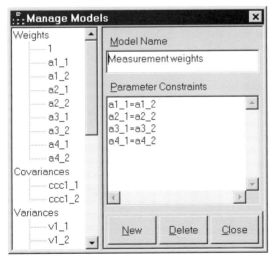

## ❑ Fit all the models and view the output

➔ Click ⌗ on the Amos Graphics toolbar to fit all models, and then click 🖹 to view the text output.

➔ In the output viewer's navigation tree, click the **Model Fit** node to expand it, and then click **CMIN**.

The **CMIN** table shows the likelihood ratio chi square statistic for each fitted model. The data do not depart significantly from any of the models. Furthermore, at each step up the hierarchy from the **Unconstrained** model to the **Measurement residuals** model, the increase in chi square is never much larger than the increase in degrees of freedom. There appears then to be no significant evidence that girls' parameter values differ from boys' parameter values.

**CMIN**

| Model | NPAR | CMIN | DF | P | CMIN/DF |
|---|---|---|---|---|---|
| Unconstrained | 26 | 16.48 | 16 | .42 | 1.03 |
| Measurement weights | 22 | 18.29 | 20 | .57 | .91 |
| Structural covariances | 19 | 22.04 | 23 | .52 | .96 |
| Measurement residuals | 13 | 26.02 | 29 | .62 | .90 |
| Saturated model | 42 | .00 | 0 | | |
| Independence model | 12 | 337.55 | 30 | .00 | 11.25 |

➔ In the navigation tree, click **AIC** under the **Model Fit** node.

**AIC** and **BCC** values indicate that the best tradeoff of model fit and parsimony is obtained by constraining all parameters to be equal across groups (the Measurement residuals model).

**AIC**

| Model | AIC | BCC | BIC | CAIC |
|---|---|---|---|---|
| Unconstrained | 68.48 | 74.12 | | |
| Measurement weights | 62.29 | 67.07 | | |
| Structural covariances | 60.04 | 64.16 | | |
| Measurement residuals | 52.02 | 54.84 | | |
| Saturated model | 84.00 | 93.12 | | |
| Independence model | 361.55 | 364.16 | | |

# Customizing the analysis

There were two opportunities to override the automatically generated cross-group constraints. In Figure 20 you could have changed the check marks in columns 1, 2, and 3, and you could have generated additional models by placing check marks in columns 4 through 8. Then in Figure 21 you could have renamed or modified any of the automatically generated models listed in the panel at the left of the path diagram.

# Model 24b: Comparing factor means

Introducing explicit means and intercepts into a model raises additional questions about which cross-group parameter constraints should be tested, and in what order. This example shows how Amos constrains means and intercepts while fitting the factor analysis model of Figure 19 to data from separate groups of girls and boys.

This is the same two-group factor analysis problem that was considered in Example 15. The results in Example 15 will be obtained here automatically.

## ❑ Specify the model

➔ Choose **File**→**Open** from the Amos Graphics menu bar.

➔ In the **Open** dialog box, double-click the file **Ex24b.amw**. If you performed a typical installation, the path will be **C:\Program Files\Amos 5\Examples\Ex24b.amw**.

**Tip:** If the last file you opened was in the Examples folder, you can open the file by double-clicking it in the Files list to the left of the Drawing Area.

The path diagram is the same for boys as for girls, and is shown in Figure 22. Some regression weights are fixed at 1. The means of all the unobserved variables are fixed at zero. In the following section, you will remove the constraints on the girls' factor means. The other constraints (the ones that you do not remove) will remain in effect throughout the analysis to follow.

*Figure 22: Two-factor model with explicit means and intercepts*

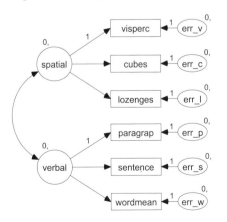

## ❑ Remove constraints on the girls' factor means

Initially, the factor means are fixed at 0 for both boys and girls. It is not possible to estimate factor means for both groups. However, Sörbom (1974) showed that, by fixing the factor means of a single group to constant values and placing suitable constraints on the regression weights and intercepts in a factor model, it is possible to obtain meaningful estimates of the factor means for all the other groups. In the present example, this means picking one group, say boys, and fixing their factor means to a constant, say 0, and then removing the constraints on the factor means of the remaining group: the girls. The constraints on regression weights and intercepts required by Sörbom's approach will be generated automatically by Amos.

The boys' factor means are already fixed at 0. To remove the constraints on the girls' factor means, do this:

➔ In the Drawing Area of the **Amos Graphics** window, double-click **Spatial**.

➔ In the **Object Properties** dialog box, click the **Parameters** tab.

➔ Select the **0** in the **Mean** box, and press the **Delete** key.

➔ With the **Object Properties** dialog box still open, click **Verbal** in the Drawing Area. This displays the properties for the **Verbal** factor in the **Object Properties** dialog box.

➔ In the **Mean** box on the **Parameters** tab, select the **0** and press the **Delete** key.

➔ Close the **Object Properties** dialog box.

Now that the constraints on the girls' factor means have been removed, the girls' and boys' path diagrams look like this:

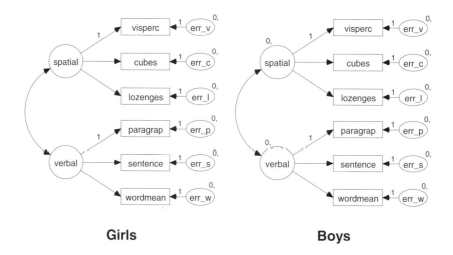

Girls                          Boys

**Tip:** To switch between path diagrams in the Drawing Area, click either **Boys** or **Girls** in the **List of Groups** pane to the left.

## ❑ Generate the cross-group constraints

➜ Click ▓ on the Amos Graphics toolbar, or choose **Model-Fit→Multiple-Group Analysis** from the menu bar.

➜ Click **OK** in the message box that appears. This opens the **Multiple-Group Analysis** dialog box.

| Multiple-Group Analysis | | | | | | | | |
|---|---|---|---|---|---|---|---|---|
| Parameter Subsets | | | | Models | | | | |
| | 1 | 2 | 3 | 4 | 5 | 6 | 7 | 8 |
| Measurement weights | ☑ | ☑ | ☑ | ☑ | ☑ | ☐ | ☐ | ☐ |
| Measurement intercepts | ☐ | ☑ | ☑ | ☑ | ☑ | ☐ | ☐ | ☐ |
| Structural weights | ☐ | ☐ | ☑ | ☑ | ☑ | ☐ | ☐ | ☐ |
| Structural intercepts | ☐ | ☐ | ☑ | ☑ | ☑ | ☐ | ☐ | ☐ |
| Structural means | ☐ | ☐ | ☑ | ☑ | ☑ | ☐ | ☐ | ☐ |
| Structural covariances | ☐ | ☐ | ☐ | ☑ | ☑ | ☐ | ☐ | ☐ |
| Structural residuals | ☐ | ☐ | ☐ | ☐ | ☑ | ☐ | ☐ | ☐ |
| Measurement residuals | ☐ | ☐ | ☐ | ☐ | ☑ | ☐ | ☐ | ☐ |

Help    Default    OK    Cancel

The default settings, as shown above, will generate the following nested hierarchy of five models:

| Model | Constraints |
|---|---|
| Model 1 (column 1) | Measurement weights (factor loadings) are equal across groups. |
| Model 2 (column 2) | All of the above, and measurement intercepts (intercepts in the equations for predicting measured variables) are equal across groups. |
| Model 3 (column 3) | All of the above, and structural means (factor means) are equal across groups. |
| Model 4 (column 4) | All of the above, and structural covariances (factor variances and covariances) are equal across groups. |
| Model 5 (column 5) | All parameters are equal across groups. |

➜ Click **OK**.

## ❑ Fit all the models

➔ Click ▦ on the Amos Graphics toolbar.

The panel at the left of the path diagram shows that two models could not be fitted to the data. The two models that could not be fitted, the **Unconstrained** model with no cross-group constraints, and the **Measurement weights** model with factor loadings held equal across groups, are unidentified.

```
XX: Unconstrained
XX: Measurement weights
OK: Measurement intercepts
OK: Structural means
OK: Structural covariances
OK: Measurement residuals
```

## ❑ View the output

➔ Click ▤ to view the text output.

➔ In the navigation tree of the output viewer, click the **Model Fit** node to expand it.

➔ Some fit measures for the four automatically generated and identified models are shown here along with fit measures for the saturated and independence models.

➔ Click **CMIN** under the **Model Fit** node.

The **CMIN** table shows that none of the generated models can be rejected when tested against the saturated model.

**CMIN**

| Model | NPAR | CMIN | DF | P | CMIN/DF |
|---|---|---|---|---|---|
| Measurement intercepts | 30 | 22.593 | 24 | .544 | .941 |
| Structural means | 28 | 30.624 | 26 | .243 | 1.178 |
| Structural covariances | 25 | 34.381 | 29 | .226 | 1.186 |
| Measurement residuals | 19 | 38.459 | 35 | .316 | 1.099 |
| Saturated model | 54 | .00 | 0 | | |
| Independence model | 24 | 337.553 | 30 | .00 | 11.252 |

On the other hand, the change in chi square (30.62 – 22.59 = 8.03) when introducing the equal-factor-means constraint looks large compared to the change in degrees of freedom (26 – 24 = 2).

→ In the navigation tree, click the **Model Comparison** node. The following table shows that this chi square difference is significant:

**Assuming model Measurement intercepts to be correct**

| Model | DF | CMIN | P | NFI Delta-1 | IFI Delta-2 | RFI rho-1 | TLI rho2 |
|-------|----|------|---|-------------|-------------|-----------|----------|
| Structural means | 2 | 8.030 | .018 | .024 | .026 | .021 | .023 |
| Structural covariances | 5 | 11.787 | .038 | .035 | .038 | .022 | .024 |
| Measurement residuals | 11 | 15.865 | .146 | .047 | .051 | .014 | .015 |

In the preceding two tables, two chi square statistics and their associated degrees of freedom are especially important. The first, $\chi^2$=22.59 with df=24, allowed accepting the hypothesis of equal intercepts and equal regression weights in the measurement model. It was important to establish the credibility of this hypothesis because without equal intercepts and equal regression weights it would be unclear that the factors have the same meaning for boys as for girls and so there would be no interest in comparing their means. The other important chi square statistic, $\chi^2$=8.03 with df=2, leads to rejection of the hypothesis that boys and girls have the same factor means.

Group differences between the boys' and girls' factor means can be determined from the girls' estimates in the **Measurement intercepts** model.

→ Select the **Measurement intercepts** model in the pane at the lower left of the output viewer.

→ In the navigation tree, click **Estimates**, and then **Scalars**, and then **Means**.

The boys' means were fixed at zero, so only the girls' means were estimated.

**Means for girls**

| | Estimate | S.E. | C.R. | P | Label |
|--|----------|------|------|---|-------|
| spatial | -1.066 | .881 | -1.209 | .226 | m1_1 |
| verbal | .956 | .521 | 1.836 | .066 | m2_1 |

These estimates were discussed in Model A of Example 15, which is identical to the present **Measurement intercepts** model. (Model B of Example 15 is identical to the present **Structural means** model.)

# Example 25: Multiple-Group Analysis

## Purpose

- Automatically implement Sörbom's alternative to analysis of covariance.

## Introduction

Example 16 demonstrates the benefits of Sörbom's approach to analysis of covariance with latent variables. Unfortunately, as Example 16 also showed, the Sörbom approach is difficult to apply, involving many steps. The present example obtains the same results as Example 16 automatically.

## The data

The Olsson (1973) data from Example 16 will be used here. The sample moments can be found in the workbook **UserGuide.xls**. Sample moments from the experimental group are in the worksheet **Olss_exp**. Sample moments from the control group are in the worksheet **Olss_cnt**.

## The model

The model was described in Example 16. The Sörbom method requires that the experimental and the control group have the same path diagram:

*Figure 23: Sörbom model for Olsson data*

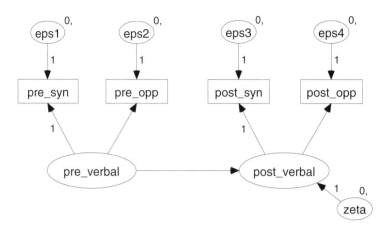

## ❑ Specify the model

➔ Choose **File→Open** from the Amos Graphics menu bar.

➔ In the **Open** dialog box, double-click the file **Ex25.amw**. If you performed a typical installation, the path will be **C:\Program Files\Amos 5\Examples\Ex25.amw**.

**Tip:** If the last file you opened was in the Examples folder, you can open the file by double-clicking it in the Files list to the left of the Drawing Area.

The path diagram is the same for the control and experimental groups, and is shown in Figure 23. Some regression weights are fixed at 1. The means of all the residual (error) variable means are fixed at 0. These constraints will remain in effect throughout the analysis to follow.

## ❑ Constrain the latent variable means and intercepts

The model in Figure 23 is unidentified and will remain unidentified for every set of cross-group constraints that Amos automatically generates. For every set of cross-group constraints, the mean of **pre_verbal** and the intercept in the equation for predicting **post_verbal** will be unidentified. In order to allow the model to be identified for at least some cross-group constraints it is necessary to pick one group, say the control group, and fix the **pre_verbal** mean and the **post_verbal** intercept to a constant, say 0.

➔ In the **List of Groups** pane to the left of the path diagram, ensure that **Control** is selected. This indicates that the path diagram for the control group is displayed in the Drawing Area.

➔ In the Drawing Area, double-click **pre_verbal**.

➔ In the **Object Properties** dialog box, click the **Parameters** tab.

➔ In the **Mean** box, type **0**.

➔ With the **Object Properties** dialog box still open, click **post_verbal** in the Drawing Area.

➔ In the **Intercept** box of the **Object Properties** dialog box, type **0**.

➔ Close the **Object Properties** dialog box.

Now, the path diagram for the control group appears as follows:

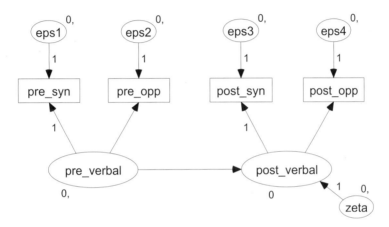

The experimental group's path diagram continues to look like Figure 23.

## ❑ Generate the cross-group constraints

➔ Click ▦ on the Amos Graphics toolbar, or choose **Model-Fit→Multiple-Group Analysis** from the menu bar.

Click **OK** in the message box that appears. This opens the **Multiple-Group Analysis** dialog box.

**Multiple-Group Analysis**

| Parameter Subsets | 1 | 2 | 3 | 4 | 5 | 6 | 7 | 8 |
|---|---|---|---|---|---|---|---|---|
| Measurement weights | ☑ | ☑ | ☑ | ☑ | ☑ | ☑ | ☑ | ☑ |
| Measurement intercepts | ☐ | ☑ | ☑ | ☑ | ☑ | ☑ | ☑ | ☑ |
| Structural weights | ☐ | ☐ | ☑ | ☑ | ☑ | ☑ | ☑ | ☑ |
| Structural intercepts | ☐ | ☐ | ☐ | ☑ | ☑ | ☑ | ☑ | ☑ |
| Structural means | ☐ | ☐ | ☐ | ☐ | ☑ | ☑ | ☑ | ☑ |
| Structural covariances | ☐ | ☐ | ☐ | ☐ | ☐ | ☑ | ☑ | ☑ |
| Structural residuals | ☐ | ☐ | ☐ | ☐ | ☐ | ☐ | ☑ | ☑ |
| Measurement residuals | ☐ | ☐ | ☐ | ☐ | ☐ | ☐ | ☐ | ☑ |

Help    Default    OK    Cancel

➔ Click **OK** to generate the following nested hierarchy of eight models:

| Model | Constraints |
|---|---|
| Model 1 (column 1) | Measurement weights (factor loadings) are constant across groups. |
| Model 2 (column 2) | All of the above, and measurement intercepts (intercepts in the equations for predicting measured variables) are constant across groups. |
| Model 3 (column 3) | All of the above, and the structural weight (the regression weight for predicting **post_verbal**) is constant across groups. |
| Model 4 (column 4) | All of the above, and the structural intercept (the intercept in the equation for predicting **post_verbal**) is constant across groups. |
| Model 5 (column 5) | All of the above, and the structural mean (the mean of **pre_verbal**) is constant across groups. |
| Model 6 (column 6) | All of the above, and the structural covariance (the variance of **pre_verbal**) is constant across groups. |
| Model 7 (column 7) | All of the above, and the structural residual (the variance of **zeta**) is constant across groups. |
| Model 8 (column 8) | All parameters are constant across groups. |

## ❑ Fit all the models

➔ Click 🎹 on the Amos Graphics toolbar to fit all models.

The panel to the left of the path diagram shows that two models could not be fitted to the data. The two models that could not be fitted, the **Unconstrained** model and the **Measurement weights** model, are unidentified.

```
XX: Unconstrained
XX: Measurement weights
OK: Measurement intercepts
OK: Structural weights
OK: Structural intercepts
OK: Structural means
OK: Structural covariances
OK: Structural residuals
OK: Measurement residuals
```

## ❑ View the output

→ Click 🖽 on the Amos Graphics toolbar to view the output.

→ In the output viewer's navigation tree, click the **Model Fit** node to expand it, and then click **CMIN**. This displays some fit measures for the seven automatically generated and identified models, along with fit measures for the saturated and independence models:

### CMIN

| Model | NPAR | CMIN | DF | P | CMIN/DF |
|---|---|---|---|---|---|
| Measurement intercepts | 22 | 34.775 | 6 | .000 | 5.796 |
| Structural weights | 21 | 36.340 | 7 | .000 | 5.191 |
| Structural intercepts | 20 | 84.060 | 8 | .000 | 10.507 |
| Structural means | 19 | 94.970 | 9 | .000 | 10.552 |
| Structural covariances | 18 | 99.976 | 10 | .000 | 9.998 |
| Structural residuals | 17 | 112.143 | 11 | .000 | 10.195 |
| Measurement residuals | 13 | 122.366 | 15 | .000 | 8.158 |
| Saturated model | 28 | .000 | 0 | | |
| Independence model | 16 | 682.638 | 12 | .000 | 56.887 |

There are many chi square statistics in this table, but only two of them matter. The Sörbom procedure comes down to two basic questions. First, does the **Structural weights** model fit? This model specifies that the regression weight for predicting **post_verbal** from **pre_verbal** be constant across groups. If the **Structural weights** model is accepted one follows up by asking whether the next model up the hierarchy, the **Structural intercepts** model, fits significantly worse. On the other hand, if the **Structural weights** model has to be rejected, one never gets to the question about the **Structural intercepts** model. Unfortunately, that is the case here. The **Structural weights** model, with $\chi^2$=36.34 and df=7, is rejected at any conventional significance level.

## ❑ Examine the modification indices

The following will let you see if it is possible to improve the fit of the **Structural weights** model.

➜ Close the output viewer.

➜ In Amos Graphics, choose **View/Set→Analysis Properties** from the menu bar.

➜ In the **Analysis Properties** dialog box, click the **Output** tab, and select the **Modification Indices** checkbox.

➜ Close the **Analysis Properties** dialog box.

➜ Click ▦ to fit all models again.

Only the modification indices for the Structural weights model need to be examined because this is this is the only model whose fit is essential to the analysis.

➜ Choose **View/Set→Text Output** from the menu bar, click **Modification Indices** in the upper left panel of the output viewer, and then click **Structural weights** in the lower left panel.

➜ Click the **Modification Indices** node to expand it, and then click **Covariances**.

As you can see, for the control group, only one modification index exceeds the default threshold of 4.

**Covariances:**

|  | M.I. | Par Change |
|---|---|---|
| eps2 <--> eps4 | 4.553 | 2.073 |

➜ Now click **experimental** in the panel on the left. For the experimental group, there are four modification indices greater than 4.

**Covariances:**

|  | M.I. | Par Change |
|---|---|---|
| eps2 <--> eps4 | 9.314 | 4.417 |
| eps2 <--> eps3 | 9.393 | -4.117 |
| eps1 <--> eps4 | 8.513 | -3.947 |
| eps1 <--> eps3 | 6.192 | 3.110 |

Of these, only two modifications have an obvious theoretical justification: allowing **eps2** to correlate with **eps4**, and allowing **eps1** to correlate with **eps3**. Between these two, allowing **eps2** to correlate with **eps4** has the larger modification index. Thus the modification indices from the control group and the experimental group both suggest allowing **eps2** to correlate with **eps4**.

## ❑ Modify the model and repeat the analysis

➔ Close the output viewer.

➔ Click ⟷ on the Amos Graphics toolbar, and then in the Drawing Area, click and drag from **eps2** to **eps4**. This connects them with a double-headed arrow.

➔ Click ⬛ on the Amos Graphics toolbar, or choose **Model-Fit→Multiple-Group Analysis** from the menu bar, then click **OK** in the message box that appears.

➔ In the **Multiple-Group Analysis** dialog box, click **OK**.

➔ Click ▦ to fit all models.

➔ Click ▦ to view the output, and use the navigation tree to view the fit measures for the Structural Weights model.

With the additional double-headed arrow connecting **eps2** and **eps4**, the **Structural weights** model has an adequate fit ($\chi^2$=3.98 with df=5).

**CMIN**

| Model | NPAR | CMIN | DF | P | CMIN/DF |
|---|---|---|---|---|---|
| Measurement intercepts | 24 | 2.797 | 4 | .59 | .699 |
| Structural weights | 23 | 3.976 | 5 | .55 | .795 |
| Structural intercepts | 22 | 55.094 | 6 | .00 | 9.182 |
| Structural means | 21 | 63.792 | 7 | .00 | 9.113 |
| Structural covariances | 20 | 69.494 | 8 | .00 | 8.687 |
| Structural residuals | 19 | 83.194 | 9 | .00 | 9.244 |
| Measurement residuals | 14 | 93.197 | 14 | .00 | 6.657 |
| Saturated model | 28 | .000 | 0 | | |
| Independence model | 16 | 682.638 | 12 | .00 | 56.887 |

Now that the **Structural weights** model fits the data, it can be asked whether the **Structural intercepts** model fits significantly worse.

**Assuming model Structural weights to be correct:**

| Model | DF | CMIN | P | NFI Delta-1 | IFI Delta-2 | RFI rho-1 | TLI rho2 |
|---|---|---|---|---|---|---|---|
| Structural intercepts | 1 | 51.118 | .000 | .075 | .075 | .147 | .150 |
| Structural means | 2 | 59.816 | .000 | .088 | .088 | .146 | .149 |
| Structural covariances | 3 | 65.518 | .000 | .096 | .097 | .139 | .141 |
| Structural residuals | 4 | 79.218 | .000 | .116 | .117 | .149 | .151 |
| Measurement residuals | 9 | 89.221 | .000 | .131 | .132 | .103 | .105 |

The **Structural intercepts** model does fit significantly worse than the **Structural weights** model. When the intercept in the equation for predicting **post_verbal** is required to be constant across groups, the chi square statistic increases by 51.12 while degrees of freedom increases by only 1. That is, the experimental group's intercept differs significantly from the control group's intercept.

The experimental group's intercept is estimated to be 3.627.

| | Estimate | S.E. | C.R. | P | Label |
|---|---|---|---|---|---|
| post_verbal | 3.627 | .478 | 7.591 | <.001 | j1_2 |
| pre_syn | 18.619 | .594 | 31.355 | <.001 | i1_1 |
| pre_opp | 19.910 | .541 | 36.781 | <.001 | i2_1 |
| post_syn | 20.383 | .535 | 38.066 | <.001 | i3_1 |
| post_opp | 21.204 | .531 | 39.908 | <.001 | i4_1 |

**Intercepts:**

Recalling that the control group's intercept was fixed at zero, it is estimated that the treatment increases **post_verbal** scores by 3.63 with **pre_verbal** "held constant."

The results obtained in the present example are identical to the results of Example 16. The **Structural weights** model is the same as Example 16's Model D. The **Structural intercepts** model is the same as Example 16's Model E.

# Appendix E: Using Fit Measures to Rank Models

In general, it is hard to pick a fit measure because there are so many to pick from. The choice gets easier when the purpose of the fit measure is to compare models to each other, rather than to judge the merit of models by an absolute standard. For example, it turns out that it does not matter whether you use **RMSEA**, **RFI** or **TLI** when rank-ordering a collection of models. Each of those three measures depends on $\hat{C}$ and $d$ only through $\hat{C}/d$, and each depends monotonically on $\hat{C}/d$. Thus each measure gives the same rank-ordering of models. For this reason, the specification search procedure reports only **RMSEA**.

- $$\text{RMSEA} = \sqrt{\frac{\hat{C} - d}{nd}} = \sqrt{\frac{1}{n}\left(\frac{\hat{C}}{d} - 1\right)}$$

- $$\text{RFI} = \rho_1 = 1 - \frac{\hat{C}/d}{\hat{C}_b/d_b}$$

- $$\text{TLI} = \rho_2 = \frac{\frac{\hat{C}_b}{d_b} - \frac{\hat{C}}{d}}{\frac{\hat{C}_b}{d_b} - 1}$$

The following fit measures depend on $\hat{C}$ and $d$ only through $\hat{C} - d$, and they depend monotonically on $\hat{C} - d$. The specification search procedure reports only **CFI** as representative of them all.

- $$\text{NCP} = \max\left(\hat{C} - d, \ 0\right)$$

- $\displaystyle \text{F0} = \hat{F}_0 = \max\left( \frac{\hat{C} - d}{n},\ 0 \right)$

- $\displaystyle \text{CFI} = 1 - \frac{\max\left(\hat{C} - d, 0\right)}{\max\left(\hat{C}_b - d_b, \hat{C} - d, 0\right)}$

- $\displaystyle \text{RNI} = 1 - \frac{\hat{C} - d}{\hat{C}_b - d_b}$  (not reported by Amos)

The following fit measures depend monotonically on $\hat{C}$, and not at all on $d$. The specification search procedure reports only $\hat{C}$ as representative of them all.

- $\displaystyle \text{CMIN} = \hat{C}$

- $\displaystyle \text{FMIN} = \frac{\hat{C}}{n}$

- $\displaystyle \text{NFI} = 1 - \frac{\hat{C}}{\hat{C}_b}$

Each of the following fit measures is a weighted sum of $\hat{C}$ and $d$, and can produce a distinct rank order of models. The specification search procedure reports each of them except for **CAIC**.

- BCC

- AIC

- BIC

- CAIC

Each of the following fit measures is capable of providing a unique rank-order of models. The rank order depends on the choice of baseline model as well. The specification search procedure does not report these measures.

- $\text{IFI} = \Delta_2$

- PNFI

- PCFI

The following fit measures are the only ones reported by Amos that are not functions of $\hat{C}$ and $d$ in the case of maximum likelihood estimation. The specification search procedure does not report these measures.

- GFI
- AGFI
- PGFI

# Appendix F: Baseline Models for Descriptive Fit Measures

Seven measures of fit, **NFI**, **RFI**, **IFI**, **TLI**, **CFI**, **PNFI**, and **PCFI**, require a "null" or "baseline" bad model against which other models can be compared. The specification search procedure offers a choice of four null, or baseline, models:

- **Null 1:** The observed variables are required to be uncorrelated. Their means and variances are unconstrained. This is the baseline "Independence" model in an ordinary Amos analysis when you do not perform a specification search.

- **Null 2:** The correlations among the observed variables are required to be equal. The means and variances of the observed variables are unconstrained.

- **Null 3:** The observed variables are required to be uncorrelated and to have zero means. Their variances are unconstrained. This is the baseline "Independence" model used by Amos 4.0.1 and earlier for models where means and intercepts are explicit model parameters.

- **Null 4:** The correlations among the observed variables are required to be equal. The variances of the observed variables are unconstrained. Their means are required to be 0.

Each null model gives rise to a different value for **NFI**, **RFI**, **IFI**, **TLI**, **CFI**, **PNFI**, and **PCFI**.

Models **Null 3** and **Null 4** are fitted during a specification search only when means and intercepts are explicitly estimated in the models you specify. The **Null 3** and **Null 4** models may be appropriate when evaluating models in which means and intercepts are constrained. There is little reason to fit the **Null 3** and **Null 4** models in the common situation where means and intercepts are not constrained but are estimated for the sole purpose of allowing maximum likelihood estimation with missing data.

To specify which baseline models you want to be fitted during specification searches, do the following:

➜ Click the **Options** button ☑ on the **Specification Search** toolbar.

➜ In the **Options** dialog box, click the **Next search** tab.

The four null models, along with the saturated model, are listed in the **Benchmark models** group.

# Appendix G: Rescaling of AIC, BCC, and BIC

The fit measures, **AIC**, **BCC**, and **BIC**, are defined in Appendix C. Each measure is of the form $\hat{C} + kq$, where $k$ takes on the same value for all models. Small values are good, reflecting a combination of good fit to the data (small $\hat{C}$) and parsimony (small $q$). The measures are used for comparing models to each other, and not for judging the merit of a single model.

Amos's specification search procedure provides three ways of rescaling these measures, which were illustrated in Examples 22 and 23. This Appendix provides formulas for the re-scaled fit measures.

In what follows, let $\text{AIC}^{(i)}$, $\text{BCC}^{(i)}$, and $\text{BIC}^{(i)}$ be the fit values for model $i$.

## Zero-based re-scaling

Because **AIC**, **BCC**, and **BIC** are used only for comparing models to each other, with smaller values being better than larger values, there is no harm in adding a constant, as in

- $\text{AIC}_0^{(i)} = \text{AIC}^{(i)} - \min_i \left[ \text{AIC}^{(i)} \right]$

- $\text{BCC}_0^{(i)} = \text{BCC}^{(i)} - \min_i \left[ \text{BCC}^{(i)} \right]$

- $\text{BIC}_0^{(i)} = \text{BIC}^{(i)} - \min_i \left[ \text{BIC}^{(i)} \right]$

The rescaled values are either zero or positive. The best model according to, say, AIC has $\text{AIC}_0 = 0$, while inferior models have positive $\text{AIC}_0$ values that reflect how much worse they are than the best model.

→ To display $\text{AIC}_0$, $\text{BCC}_0$ and $\text{BIC}_0$ after a specification search, click ☑ on the **Specification Search** toolbar, and then on the **Current results** tab of the **Options** dialog box, click **Zero-based (min = 0)**.

## Akaike weights and Bayes factors (sum = 1)

By selecting **Akaike weights and Bayes factors (sum = 1)** on the **Current results** tab of the **Options** dialog box, one obtains the rescaling

- $$\text{AIC}_p^{(i)} = \frac{e^{-\text{AIC}^{(i)}/2}}{\sum_m e^{-\text{AIC}^{(m)}/2}}$$

- $$\text{BCC}_p^{(i)} = \frac{e^{-\text{BCC}^{(i)}/2}}{\sum_m e^{-\text{BCC}^{(m)}/2}}$$

- $$\text{BIC}_p^{(i)} = \frac{e^{-\text{BIC}^{(i)}/2}}{\sum_m e^{-\text{BIC}^{(m)}/2}}$$

Each of these rescaled measures sums to 1 across models. The rescaling is performed only after an exhaustive specification search. If a heuristic search is carried out, or if a positive value is specified for **Retain only the best ___ models**, then the summation in the denominator cannot be calculated and rescaling is not performed. The $\text{AIC}_p^{(i)}$ are called *Akaike weights* by Burnham and Anderson (1998). $\text{BCC}_p^{(i)}$ has the same interpretation as $\text{AIC}_p^{(i)}$. Within the Bayesian framework and under suitable assumptions with equal prior probabilities for the models, the $\text{BIC}_p^{(i)}$ are approximate posterior probabilities (Raftery, 1993, 1995).

# Akaike weights and Bayes factors (max = 1)

By selecting **Akaike weights and Bayes factors (max = 1)** on the **Current results** tab of the **Options** dialog box, one obtains the rescaling

- $\text{AIC}_L^{(i)} = \dfrac{e^{-\text{AIC}^{(i)}/2}}{\max\limits_{m}\left[e^{-\text{AIC}^{(m)}/2}\right]}$

- $\text{BCC}_L^{(i)} = \dfrac{e^{-\text{BCC}^{(i)}/2}}{\max\limits_{m}\left[e^{-\text{BCC}^{(m)}/2}\right]}$

- $\text{BIC}_L^{(i)} = \dfrac{e^{-\text{BIC}^{(i)}/2}}{\max\limits_{m}\left[e^{-\text{BIC}^{(m)}/2}\right]}$

The best model according to, say, **AIC** has $\text{AIC}_L = 1$, while inferior models have $\text{AIC}_L$ between 0 and 1. See Burnham and Anderson (1998) for further discussion of $\text{AIC}_L$, and Raftery (1993, 1995) and Madigan and Raftery (1994) for further discussion of $\text{BIC}_L$.

# Bibliography

Akaike, H. (1978). A Bayesian analysis of the minimum AIC procedure. *Annals of the Institute of Statistical Mathematics*, *30*, 9-14.

Arbuckle, J. L. (Unpublished, 1991). Bootstrapping and model selection for analysis of moment structures.

Bentler, P. M. & Bonett, D. G. (1980). Significance tests and goodness of fit in the analysis of covariance structures. *Psychological Bulletin*, *88*, 588–606.

Bentler, P. (1989). *EQS structural equations program manual*. Los Angeles, CA: BMDP Statistical Software.

Bollen, K. (1989). *Structural equations with latent variables*. New York: Wiley.

Bozdogan, H. (1987). Model selection and Akaike's information criterion AIC: the general theory and its analytical extensions. *Psychometrika*, *52*, 345-370.

Burnham, K.P. & Anderson, D.R. (1998). *Model selection and inference: A practical information-theoretic approach*. New York: Springer-Verlag.

Cattell, R.B. (1966). The scree test for the number of factors. *Multivariate Behavioral Research*, 1, 245-276.

Felson, R.B. & Bohrnstedt, G.W. (1979). "Are the good beautiful or the beautiful good?" The relationship between children's perceptions of ability and perceptions of physical attractiveness. *Social Psychology Quarterly*, *42*, 386-392.

Furnival, G.M. & Wilson, R.W. (1974). Regression by leaps and bounds. *Technometrics*, *16*, 499-511.

Hoeting, J.A., Madigan, D., Raftery, A.E. & Volinsky, C.T. (1999). Bayesian model averaging: A tutorial. *Statistical Science*, *14*, 382-417.

Holzinger, K.J. & Swineford, F.A. (1939). A study in factor analysis: The stability of a bifactor solution. *Supplementary Educational Monographs, No. 48*. Chicago: University of Chicago, Dept. of Education.

Hu, L. & Bentler, P.M. (1999). Cutoff criteria for fit indices in covariance structure analysis: conventional criteria versus new alternatives. *Structural Equation Modeling, 6*, 1-55.

Jamison, C. & Scogin, F. (1995). The outcome of cognitive bibliotherapy with depressed adults. *Journal of Consulting and Clinical Psychology, 63*, 644-650.

Jöreskog, K.G. & Sörbom, D. (1996). *LISREL 8 User's reference guide*. Chicago: Scientific Software.

Judd, C.M. & Milburn, M.A. (1980). The structure of attitude systems in the general public: Comparisons of a structural equation model. *American Sociological Review, 45*, 627-643.

Kline, R. B. (1998). *Principles and practice of structural equation modeling*. New York: The Guilford Press.

Loehlin, J. C. (1992). *Latent variable models: an introduction to factor, path, and structural analysis (2nd edition)*. Hillsdale, New Jersey: Erlbaum.

MacCallum, R. (1986). Specification searches in covariance structure modeling. *Psychological Bulletin, 100*, 107-120.

MacCallum, R., Wegener, D., Uchino, B. & Fabrigar, L. (1993). The problem of equivalent models in applications of covariance structure analysis. *Psychological Bulletin, 114*, 185-199.

Madigan, D. & Raftery, A.E. (1994). Model selection and accounting for model uncertainty in graphical models using Occam's window. *Journal of the American Statistical Association, 89*, 1535-1546.

Matsumoto, M. & Nishimura, T. (1998). Mersenne twister: A 623-dimensionally equidistributed uniform pseudo-random number generator. *ACM Transactions on Modeling and Computer Simulation, 8*, 3-30.

Olsson, S. (1973). *An Experimental Study of the Effects of Training on Test Scores and Factor Structure*. Uppsala, Sweden: University of Uppsala, Department of Education.

Raftery, A.E. (1993). Bayesian model selection in structural equation models. In K.A. Bollen & J.S. Long (Eds.) *Testing structural equation* models. Newbury Park, California: Sage, 163–180.

Raftery, A.E. (1995). Bayesian model selection in social research. In P.V. Marsden (Ed.) *Sociological Methodology 1995*. San Francisco: Jossey-Bass, 111-163.

Salhi, S. (1998). Heuristic search methods. In G.A. Marcoulides (Ed.) *Modern methods for business research*. Mahwah, NJ: Erlbaum, 147-175.

Schwarz, G. (1978). Estimating the dimension of a model. *The Annals of Statistics, 6*, 461–464.

Sörbom, D. (1974). A general method for studying differences in factor means and factor structure between groups. *British Journal of Mathematical and Statistical Psychology, 27*, 229-239.

Spirtes, P., Scheines, R. & Glymour, C. (1990). Simulation studies of the reliability of computer-aided model specification using the TETRAD II, EQS, and LISREL programs. *Sociological Methods and Research, 19*, 3-66.

Steiger, J. H. (1990). Structural model evaluation and modification: An interval estimation approach. *Multivariate Behavioral Research, 25*, 173–180.

Wichman, B. & Hill, I. (1982). An efficient and portable pseudo-random number generator. Algorithm AS 183. *Applied Statistics, 31*, 188-190.

# Index

Burnham, K.P., 19, 21
C, 27
  best fit graph for, 32
  scatterplot for, 26
  scree plot for, 34
C/df, 30
  best fit graph for, 33
  scatterplot for, 30
CAIC, 78
candidate models. *See* models
Cattell, R.B., 1, 35
C-df, 29
  best fit graph for, 33
  scatterplot for, 30
  scree plot for, 35
CFI, 77, 81
Chart FX file format, 31
chi square statistic, 62, 73, 76
CMIN, 62, 78
comparative model fit summaries, 1
confirmatory specification searches, 14
constraints
  automatically generating, 58
  cross-group, 2
  removing, 64
  setting manually, 62
critical ratios, 1
cross-group constraints, 2, 57
  automatically generating, 58
  setting manually, 62
data from multiple groups, 2
discrepancy functions, 18
display options
  alternatives to color, 5
  for Plot window, 31
Drawing Area
  Files list, 37
  showing or hiding variable labels, 10
equivalent candidate models, 49
evaluation tools for models, 1
exhaustive specification searches, 52
exploratory
  factor analysis, 2, 43
  specification searches, 36

F0, 77
factor analysis
  exploratory, 2
  factor variances and covariances, 59
  multiple group, 57
factor loadings, 59
factor means
  comparing, 63
  removing constraints, 64
Felson, R.B., 13, 36
fit measures, 77
  AGFI, 79
  AIC, 78
  BIC, 78
  CAIC, 78
  C-df, 29
  CFI, 2, 77
  CMIN, 78
  F0, 77
  FMIN, 78
  GFI, 79
  IFI, 78
  NCP, 77
  NFI, 78
  PCFI, 78
  PGFI, 79
  PNFI, 78
  RFI, 77
  RMSEA, 77
  RNI, 77
  TLI, 77
fitting all models, 62
FMIN, 78
forwards heuristic specification searches, 52
Furnival, G.M., 47
generated models, 18, 60
GFI, 79
graphs
  adding axis titles, 31
  best fit graphs, 32
  changing fonts, 31
  choosing a background color, 31
  formatting options, 31

fitting with subsets of, 2
many, 36
output viewer
file format, 5
navigating, 3, 66
parsing XML output, 5
popup menu, 4
toolbar, 4
viewing output in a Web browser, 5
parameters
determining number to use, 26
estimates, 19
limiting, 47
point of diminishing returns, 35
viewing those affected by cross-group
constraints, 60
path diagrams
making arrows optional, 2, 14, 15
making arrows required, 15
viewing factor variances and
covariances, 60
viewing generated models, 18
viewing measurement residuals, 60
viewing structural covariances, 60
PCFI, 78, 81
PGFI, 79
plot points
changing fonts, 31
showing or hiding labels, 31
Plot window
adding axis titles, 31
adjusting the zoom level, 31
best fit graphs, 32, 33
changing fonts, 31
choosing a background color, 31
displaying print preview, 32
displaying vertical and horizontal grids,
31
formatting options, 31
modifying axis and graph titles, 31
printing the graph, 32
scatterplots, 26
scree plots, 34
showing or hiding point labels, 31

showing or hiding the toolbar, 31
PNFI, 78, 81
point of diminishing returns, 26, 33, 35
posterior probabilities, 21
prior probabilities, 21
program defaults, resetting, 16
program options, setting, 16
programming reference documentation,
10
Raftery, A.E., 22, 24
random number generation
Mersenne Twister, 10
Wichman-Hill, 10
regression weights
in the measurement part of the model,
59
making optional, 45
required arrows, 15
rescaled measures, 83
rescaling Bayes factors, 24
RFI, 77, 81
RMSEA, 77
RNI, 77
Salhi, S., 51
scatterplots
about, 26
C as fit measure, 26
C/df, 30
C-df, 29
changing display options, 31
constant fit, 28, 30
exporting as Chart FX file, 31
Schwarz, G., 24
scree plots
about, 34, 35
in principal components analysis versus
SEM, 35
scree tests, 1
SEM, defined, 1
Sörbom, D., 1, 50, 64, 69
Specification Search window
displaying, 14
toolbar, 15
specification searches, 13